The Unturned Stone

A Revolution in Preventative Healthcare

The Discovery of the Map of the Human Body-Field and the Development of the NES-Professional™

By Harry Massey and Peter Fraser

1

Table of Contents

Acknowledgements

The authors would like to thank the following people for their contributions both in helping create the NES-Professional™ and NES Infoceuticals and in helping with the writing of this book. Oliver Bradbury for the relentless pace he kept up in producing graphics over an intense six-month period; Ellen Brown and Dr Heather Went for assisting with the research and helping shape many chapters of this book; and Dr Julian Kenyon for introducing Peter Fraser and Harry Massey in the first place. We are also eternally grateful for the letters and telephone calls of support we receive from those benefiting from NES.

Note to Readers

The following information is the opinion of the authors and outlines the foundation of their bio-energetic model of the human body-field. It should be viewed as such and not as medical advice, diagnosis, or treatment. We strongly advise anyone who is concerned about personal health issues to seek the advice of a qualified healthcare professional.

Section A

Introduction to Energetic Medicine

Introduction

"Consciousness is the quantum connection between the numerous layers making up the quantum machine."

– Fred Alan Wolf, *Taking the Quantum Leap*

Most of us to some degree or another have either heard of or experienced homeopathy, acupuncture, Traditional Chinese Medicine, herbalism and other alternative modalities. Some of us stay on top of the latest breakthroughs in "frontier" healing, such as energy healing, healing at a distance (using intention to affect another person) and the effects of prayer on healing. But few of us are aware of the current research into biophysics, where advances are being made in understanding how the cells of the body emit weak levels of light and how quantum fields, in addition to chemical processes, control physiology. Nutri-Energetics Systems™ is at the forefront of this integration of physics and biology, having formulated a comprehensive theory of the quantum electrodynamic (QED) processes in the body. We have also created a computerized system to analyze the QED body-field and developed a method of reliably imprinting corrective QED information into preparations, called the NES Infoceuticals, to help people achieve better health.

This book shows how all of this became possible. It begins with the story of Harry Massey's struggle to recover from Chronic Fatigue Syndrome, his subsequent journey of discovery into both energetic medicine and Peter Fraser's groundbreaking theory of the quantum electrodynamic body-field and its implications for preventative healthcare. It continues by explaining the foundation of the most progressive preventative health system to date—the NES-Professional System™.

Chapter 1
The Story of Harry Massey and the Creation of Nutri-Energetics

"[I]f only doctors (and many other scientists) knew enough current physics, so much that seems strange and therefore improbable would yield to common sense inquiry."

– Dr. Keith Scott-Mumby, *Virtual Medicine*

Harry Massey and Peter Fraser suffered from severe Chronic Fatigue Syndrome (CFS) for seven and thirteen years, respectively. Their search for healing set them both on a path of independent research. This book is the culmination of their experiences and research. Between them, they had tried almost every type of therapy imaginable to no real avail, and they were determined to get to the root causes of their disease. The following is Harry Massey's story of that healing journey, told in his own words.

After school, at age 18, I spent a gap year teaching fifteen-year-olds sailing and kayaking in Australia, and then bought a car and travelled up the coast of Australia with two friends. Sometime during this trip, I was bitten by some kind of insect and I suffered a terrible fever for two weeks. Peter would later identify this bite as the source of a Flavi virus, a factor in CFS. Two months later, I ended up in hospital in Cairns with severe chest pains and swollen lips. Every time I inhaled, I felt as if I were breathing in glass. It seemed that the infection from two months before had begun to affect my immune system, causing severe allergic reactions to things that had not been a problem before.

When I returned home to England and enrolled in university, I was not back to my normally healthy self but I felt reasonably well. For the next two years of university life, I did fairly well.

Occasionally, if I was overdoing it, the chest pain returned and my lips swelled up again and I felt terrible. Otherwise, I was fit. I was able to indulge my passion for rock climbing and even became president of the climbing club. I was quite skilled at blocking off anything else that was going on, including danger, so as to concentrate on the matter at hand. This personality trait would prove invaluable later in helping me through some very tough years of being extremely ill. How good was I at ignoring pain? Well, three occasions are particularly memorable. One involved a thirty-foot fall I took while climbing. Another time I took a sixty-foot fall when a peg came loose in the ice. I did not discover until five years later, when having an X-ray for an unrelated matter, that I had fractured my back. I had just gotten up and carried on—not a behaviour I recommend. I also took up paragliding and on one rather gusty day in the Alps, when coming out of a thermal, I hit an enormous downdraft that completely collapsed my paraglider, pushing it behind and beneath me. I fell like a stone, with the paraglider effectively turning into a bag of washing. Beneath me was a castle that was halfway up the mountain, perched on a cliff. Just before I would have hit the castle, I managed to get control of the collapsed paraglider and turn it into a stable enough shape to push me over the castle walls and out beyond the cliff face. I survived the 500-foot free-fall drop, carried on gliding, and landed twenty minutes later. Why? Although shaken up, I knew that if I had landed immediately after the free fall I would have found it very difficult to ever paraglide again.

Soon I was not able to ignore my health. The serious problems started towards the end of my university years, where I was gradually worn down by excess exercise, overwork and the recurring viral infection. By that time, I was struggling most of the time: my chest screamed with every breath, my glands were throbbing and my brain was swimming in a cloud. Still, I kept on going.

I can only describe the next six years by likening them to being under an all-encompassing dark cloud, one that you hope one day will pass. No matter how sick I felt, I clung onto the knowledge that life had been good before and that it could be again, and I endeavoured to try everything and anything I could to get better. However, nothing worked and I grew progressively more ill. I sometimes managed to do some incredible things (for someone in that condition) in the beginning years of the illness. For example, I did a summer season in the Alps climbing many mountains, including the overhanging southeast face of the Dent du Geant, a 4000-meter peak. However, I ended up so exhausted by the end of that season that I got stuck in a tent on Lake Annecy and could not move out of it for a week. I survived on the food I had in a cool box (bread, tuna and dried bananas) before finally summoning up enough energy to get to my car and drive home. During that drive, I had to stop every hour to rest for twenty minutes before continuing. At that early stage of my deterioration, I believed I could cure myself by eating healthy food and exercising regularly, but ultimately I succeeded only in making myself worse. All my activity was just another load that my body did not have the energy to deal with.

I continued to struggle on. I started an MBA, but within one week, I knew that I did not have the energy to follow it through. Instead of quitting, however, I split the course over two years. Even doing this did not help much. Finding the energy and focus to study was the most difficult struggle I have ever put myself through. In the second year of that course, I was truly getting desperate about my health. I could hardly drag myself to lectures and soon was pretty much just staying home, in my house near the university. I finally took a radical course of action in my quest for a cure: I undertook a four-week water fast at a clinic in South Africa, on the recommendation of a friend who claimed to have been cured of CFS by going to the same clinic. What I did not know was that while I was at the clinic doing my fast, she had become ill again.

During the time in South Africa, my weight went from 11 stone to just over 8 stone. I had completely bought into the theory that fasting can detoxify the body and rid it of all bugs. Later I would learn from NES research that fasting can help the body shed some toxins, but mostly those from fat; however, some of the more nasty environmental toxins around today do serious genetic damage and fasting does little to remove these toxins or correct the problems they cause. NES would show that fasting also does little to rid the body of pleomorphic and viral organisms. The one thing that the water fast did accomplish was completely disgusting! It rid my body of hordes of parasites. My body was riddled with them and bucketful after bucketful of white jelly-like masses came out over a period of four weeks. That explained all the years of being doubled over in pain with no explanation (even stool tests had come up blank for parasites).

Ultimately the fasting was unsuccessful and because of all the weight I had lost while on it, I was actually considerably more ill than I had been before. What followed was a period during which I can properly say I was disabled. I could do very little at all. I was not able to attend a single lecture when I returned home to school. Still, with a great deal of help from my fellow MBA students at Southampton University (and here I would like to thank Becky and Simon), I managed to finish the course and gain an MBA.

My journey back to health took me on many mind trips as I explored one avenue after another. I accumulated shelves of books about nutrition, herbal medicine, yoga, Hulda Clark, diets, juicing, Gerson, kombucha tea, ozone therapy, chelation, energetic medicine, psychotherapy, hypnotism, I CHING, raw food and on and on. I even started a course in nutritional therapy, with thoughts of becoming a practitioner once I was better. I did not get permanently better. I tried all of these things, to a greater or lesser degree, and most at some level do have merit. However, not a single practitioner or book could ever explain to me what was *really* going on in my body.

Different groups gave different explanations for my health problems. The raw food people said it was because we came from apes and should be eating mostly raw vegetables and fruit and the book I read was full of very good arguments as to why this is so. The blood group people said our diets should be dictated by our blood type, with equally good arguments. Gerson suggested that coffee enemas and drinking juices for a year would do the trick. Acupuncturists said that the Governor meridian had excess yin, and psychologists said that the problem stemmed from not letting go of the past. Nevertheless, none of these explanations truly helped me understand what was going on in my body. Besides, how could they all be right?

I was confident there had to be a system that could explain the physiology, what had gone wrong, and how to set it right. Energetic medicine seemed to provide the best answer although for the uninitiated wandering through this field is a mind trip in itself. I come from a fairly conservative background, having studied mathematics, physics, and economics, securities, futures, and having earned an MBA. These are all pretty rigid disciplines and when I first came across energetic medicine, it was not something I was able to believe readily. I am someone who needs explanations and finds it very easy to see loopholes in any theory or argument. The explanations given for the first energetic medical devices I came across, a variety of diagnostic and treatment machines, were pretty thin; they mostly revolved around words such as "frequency" and "oscillations." However, being prepared to give everything a fair evaluation, I endured the mind trip, purchased some of this equipment, and even ended up marketing a variety of devices through the Internet. The deeper I got into these "energy technologies," the more I saw that there was enough evidence to say truthfully that they worked to some degree, but there were not any satisfying explanations from practitioners or the developers as to how or why they worked.

That is when I met Peter Fraser. I was introduced to Peter through a mutual colleague, Dr Julian Kenyon. At that time, Peter had been working on a theory of the human body-field and had come up with some "remedies." He used his knowledge to cure me—and he could explain how and why. Eventually, we set out together to explore ways to turn his biophysical theory of the human body-field into an overall health system. His theory not only could explain pathology, but also how homeopathy and Chinese medicine work in ways that had not been described before. But most importantly, it represented a revolutionary way to undertake preventative health screening and then treat people so they did not become sick in the first place.

For the record, so you can map the journey from where I started to where I am today, I invite you to review the following list of my physical status while ill:

- The lowest magnesium blood count on record, which no amount of IVs were able to correct (in fact, it went down further over this period)
- Severe chest pains

- Gallbladder pains
- Swollen glands
- Extreme fatigue: for three years I couldn't walk beyond 100 meters without collapsing for the rest of the day
- Parasite infection
- Sluggish cognitive function and poor memory

Peter's system of testing showed that I was heavily polluted with environmental toxins—particularly cadmium, dioxins, radiation, organochlorides and phosphates. My immunity was deteriorated in energy "compartments" 4, 10 and 11. In the NES model, "energy compartments" are pathways in the body that regulate information at the level of quantum electrodynamics and also direct physiological processes; there are 12 of them. (These "compartments" are now called Energetic Integrators.) This reduced immunity led to a proliferation of viruses, especially the Bunya virus and Flavi virus, (of which both groups of viruses have been found to be related to ME/CFS), found in Energetic Integrator 8. However, radiation, organochlorides and phosphates had also caused them to go higher, forming many pleomorphic organisms found in Energetic Integrator 10. The body is normally able to recognize and can attempt to deal with organisms when they show up in their usual energy compartments. However, because of the effects of environmental pollution, these organisms can mutate and move to Integrator 10, where the body no longer has a viable system to deal with them and so the immune system is in a constant state of battle against them. The body simply cannot make the correct antibodies when organisms, or pleomorphic organisms, are entrenched in an Integrator where they should not be. This struggle results in constant feelings of fatigue, low-grade fever and even depression.

The main distortions in Energetic Integrators 4, 10 and 11 in my body-field relate to hormones (EI 11 being related to the regulation of male hormones) and these distortions caused severe stress, which in turn affected EI 1, 7 and 12. EI 7 affects the cerebral cortex and, as such, contributed to the impairment of my mental functioning, dyslectic tendencies and tremors in my hands.

I did not have to understand about all of the Energetic Integrators to be treated. (And since the development of the NES–Professional assessment system, neither do you!) I trusted Peter to treat me and he let me know that the process might take many months. He started by reducing the overall stress level on my body-field. This meant using the Infoceuticals every day to correct Energetic Integrators 1, 7 and 12; in fact, I often took the Infoceutical drops more than once a day to help reduce emotional stress and regain proper mental functioning. Infoceuticals are a liquid that is imprinted with specific quantum electrodynamic (QED) information and are taken as drops in water. He also straight away tackled the Bunya and Flavi viruses, a major factor in CFS in many patients. This process brought on a ten-day period of flu. As my immune system began to get the proper QED information it needed to function well, it began to manufacture the correct antibodies to attack the virus. Testing two weeks later showed a complete remission of the virus. Although I sometimes still felt incredibly tired, the continual flu-like feelings and swollen glands of the previous six years were gone. It was at about this time that I really started to believe in what Peter was doing and made a commitment to myself to follow his protocol through to the end.

Peter continued to recommend Infoceuticals. When we dealt with those that affected a combination of EI 1, 7 and 12, I began unblocking years of bottled up emotions. I began to get amazing flashbacks and realizations (mostly in dreams) of the significance of events that had shaped my life, accompanied by what I can only describe as a sort of peace or feeling of resolution for each one. The best part of all was that I was no longer terrified of driving. In the depths of being ill, I pretty much gave up driving, but there were many times when I had little choice and was constantly getting lost, frustrated and narrowly avoiding accidents. I can honestly say I hated driving. However, as a result of the Infoceuticals treatment it once again became a pleasure.

The next area we worked on was the Energetic Drivers in order to help the body-field generate its own energy and, hence, accelerate the benefits of the other Infoceuticals. We now use the Drivers first in our NES protocol; our research has come a long way since these early days! During the first session with the Heart Driver, I noticed a twinge of pain in my chest within thirty minutes, and Peter explained that this was the cadmium being pushed out of the heart. I noticed that this occurred on the next two occasions that I used it, but in a more gentle way. The Lung Driver (my lungs were full of cadmium from years of smoking) caused me to cough up lots of pollution-filled mucus, and I began to feel I was breathing properly again after all those years of shallow and difficult breathing. The best bit of all though, was from using the Nervous System Driver for a few weeks. I noticed a really peculiar change. I had gone from being permanently wired and then completely drained to actually feeling relaxed and having the most normal sleep I had experienced in years. I was still tired, but it was a relaxed sort of tired, almost as if my body was finally catching up on years' worth of rest. I would almost say that the ridiculous drive to keep going had finally stopped and that my body now knew it was time to recuperate. I was, of course, trying at the same time to get a business off the ground, but I was suddenly very much more relaxed about it and, as a result, I was able to produce a much higher quality of work. Just for the record, as a rule I do not recommend doing this amount of work while recovering from illness. The more energy left for helping you to heal, the better. I am quite convinced I would have recovered more quickly if I had not been pushing myself to start a business.

Next came the Stomach Driver. If ever you want proof that the Nutri-Energetics Infoceuticals work, try the Stomach Driver and see what colour your stools are! Realistically, not everyone experiences the same effects, but there is a pattern or a norm and Stomach Driver can have immediate and quite noticeable effects. I was always having stomachaches—sometimes so bad that I was bent double—and there was no obvious explanation. The morning after starting the Stomach Driver, my stools were jet black and ... well, I will just say it ... quite smelly. This lasted for a few days as my small intestine and colon were shedding toxins straight out of my body. Each subsequent time I took the Stomach Driver there were fewer and fewer toxins to be released, and soon my stomach pains subsided. This Infoceutical is not designed specifically to kill pathogens in the stomach; however, pathogens have a tendency to live in this terrain and once the environment is cleaned up (e.g., the pollutants have been removed from your stomach), their population diminishes back to normal. The bloating and stomach pains that I had experienced for years disappeared over the following months.

There was still more healing to do. The next stage of my NES protocol was to correct the serious errors that had occurred in Energetic Integrators 4, 10 and 11. After taking these specific Infoceuticals, I noticed that I was able to concentrate properly again, in fact, without these Infoceuticals I do not think I would have been in any shape mentally to have written this book. However, what was also striking was that my balance and coordination returned to normal. At long last I could begin to climb again. Not only that, but in just five months I had not only regained my former climbing skill and strength but also surpassed them. For the previous six years, pretty much any attempt at exercise always ended in one step forward and three steps back. Suddenly it became three steps forward and one step back when I particularly overdid it. I had a huge amount of fitness to regain. After dropping to just over eight stone two years before, I had very little muscle mass, and when I first attempted to go climbing, I had so little leg muscle that I could hardly bear to be lowered off the top as the harness cut off all circulation and I was in agony. I cannot really describe the incredible amount of fitness that I have regained.

Another major effect that I noticed was that by the time I returned to the United Kingdom in April 2003, my hands and feet no longer felt cold. Also, for the first time I did not sneeze the whole time that I was at home due to unknown allergies (now revealed as allergies to house dust or dog hair).

While I continually improved, there were rather odd setbacks, or what I took to be setbacks. For example, an old climbing wrist and forearm injury flared up again. Thinking laterally, I tried a different approach in trying to make it better. The muscle around that area was not as fully developed as on my other forearm and I also had incurred a shoulder injury from one, if not all, of those falls years ago. From the Chinese Medicine perspective, I knew the Triple Heater meridian on the top of my right arm and also my Colon meridian were pretty sore and had been for years. These seemed connected to problems in my colon, which over the years had been plenty, and I assumed that the shoulder injury was blocking the information pathways of both meridians. I started taking lots of Energetic Integrator 1 to help the colon meridian, which was where the pain was, followed by Energetic Integrator 9 also a tender spot on the Triple Heater's meridian, which is located on the upper arm. The next week I went to my local climbing wall and experienced no pain. Over the next few weeks, I also noticed my forearm filling out, where the tender spot had been. The only explanation I can give for this is that once the appropriate conditions for repair had been put in place or, saying it another way, once the QED information pathways had been corrected, my body took over and healed itself.

I was now ready for more specific detoxification Infoceuticals to clean up any remaining toxins. I am lucky enough to have a fairly lean build; however, knowing that many toxins are stored in fatty tissues, which include the brain and nervous system, I decided to take heavy dosages of the Fat Detoxification Infoceuticals. I took this Infoceutical several times a day for ten days and I can report that I have never experienced such a detoxification! It was quite amazing! I had extremely sore lips, a very dry mouth, sore liver and kidneys and green and black fatty stools. It was also a fairly emotional ride and I consumed frequent doses of Energetic Integrators 1, 7, 12 and many anti-oxidants. I must emphasize that we do not recommend mega-dosages of the Infoceuticals because more is not better with NES. Admittedly, Peter and I often experiment on ourselves with large doses just so we know the maximum effect the Infoceuticals can have. The Infoceuticals are not pharmacological or homeopathic, they contain the information—the QED instructions—to repair damage caused by various types of shock to the body-field and they are not toxic, even in large amounts. However, our research has shown that for the majority of the Infoceuticals, there is no benefit to taking more than 28 drops per dose. Once past this number of drops, there is simply no additional effect or benefit. The frequency of dosage, however, can matter: the more frequent the dose, the more quickly or heavily an effect may be felt.

The most important effect that I noticed was that I no longer desired fatty foods, whereas before I had always put a lot of butter on toast or ate many eggs. My whole body had also shed weight, with my gut going back to normal. However, the best bit for me was that I was able to climb harder. I just felt light when mucking around on the wall. I used to be able to eat and eat and not really gain much energy from the food. Now that my liver was suddenly able to process fats properly again, I not only felt less hungry and lost excess weight, but my body was able to detoxify itself naturally and my energy level skyrocketed.

Since those days, I have taken every single Infoceutical and can say without question that I have noticed improvements in my health from all of them, albeit some of them more dramatic than others. I have gone from living a pretty hopeless existence to not only having regained my health, but also having become more energetic, intelligent and emotionally balanced. The effect of the NES Infoceuticals is holistic on the body. All I can say is, "Thanks, Peter!"

Peter's own journey about healing from Chronic Fatigue Syndrome is another story for another time. Here it is sufficient to say that it is my hope and Peter's that through the Nutri-Energetics Systems, others may benefit—not only in regaining well-being but also in preventing the loss of health in the first place. The real beauty of NES is as a preventative measure. The following chapters in Section A are meant to serve as an introduction to both energetic medicine and the physics and biophysical science that gives it its foundation. This information may take you far out of your comfort zone for it shows why the conventional worldview held by so many mainstream biologists cannot explain the causes of illness and, hence, cannot devise real long-term treatments or cures. This information prepares you for Sections B and C, where we describe our revolutionary theory of the quantum electrodynamic body-field and how it relates to healing.

Chapter 2
Information Theory and the Zero Point Field

"To the powerful theories of chemistry and physics must be added a late arrival: a theory of information. Nature must be interpreted as matter, energy, and information."

– Jeremy Campbell, *Grammatical Man*

The first paradigm shift in the modern understanding of reality occurred when Newtonian physics was modified by Einstein's theory of relativity. Newton saw nature as consisting of many related physical objects in motion. Newtonian physics emphasized entities rather than organization, and local systems rather than their relation to the total field.

In the early 1900's, Nobel Prize-winners Max Planck, Albert Einstein, Louis de Broglie and others startled the scientific world with their discoveries regarding energy. In 1925, de Broglie postulated that the electron, which moves about a positively charged nucleus in an atom, is not a "particle" but is a nonmaterial "wave." That meant that matter, when reduced to its smallest component, was only energy and that everything in the universe was a state of energy, including the human body.

Einstein showed that the behaviour of a particle is not independent of the field, but is conditioned and determined by it. Field physics recognizes the existence of many fields that contain particles that interact with each other. These range from the tiny gravitational fields within atoms to the vast ones of planetary systems. The Nobel Prize-winning English mathematician Paul Dirac pioneered the first quantum field theory. According to this theory, particles cannot be separated from the surrounding space, which constitutes a continuous field including all of material existence. Matter and light have both particle properties and wave or field properties. Particles

24

are merely condensations in the field, rather like chunks of ice formed in an ocean of waves. Since the work of Dirac, the dual nature of light as wave and particle has been free of paradox for those who can follow the mathematics. Richard Feynman, another Nobel Prize winner, and others expanded on Dirac's work to create the theory of quantum electrodynamics (QED). This describes the interaction of light and matter with remarkable accuracy, and these field effects are the ones that led Peter Fraser to his revolutionary understanding of the human body-field.

Another paradigm shift has now occurred, once again startling the scientific world—information theory and the concept of the Zero Point Field. The Zero Point Field is an underlying sea of energy that pervades all of existence. This concept and others have formed the basis for new discoveries that have been reported in major journals and newspapers including *Science, Scientific American* and *The New York Times.* Modern information theory neither finds at the most basic level of reality particles nor waves, but rather quantum probability fields or information fields, which materialize out of the vacuum whenever we interact with it.

Discovery of the Zero Point Field grew out of speculation concerning the vacuum. According to Dr. Timothy Boyer, writing in *Scientific American,* in the seventeenth century it was thought that a totally empty volume of space could be created by simply removing all matter, including all gases. Later, in the nineteenth century, it became apparent that this "vacuum" was not actually empty but contained thermal radiation, although researchers thought cooling, taking the temperature to absolute zero might eliminate this radiation. Since then, however, it has been shown both theoretically and experimentally that there is a non-thermal radiation in the vacuum that persists even if the temperature is lowered to absolute zero. The "vacuum" underlying matter, it seems, is not a vacuum at all but contains particles and waves that spontaneously pop in and out of existence, forming an underlying field. Researcher Thomas Valone, of the Integrity Research Institute, explains, "On an infinitesimally small scale ... quantum fluctuations produce a foam of erupting and collapsing virtual particles, visualized as a topographic distortion of the fabric of space-time."

Consciousness became an unavoidable element in the scientific scheme of things because of the Uncertainty Principle: the observer was found to affect the observed. Norman Friedman, in *Bridging Science and Spirit*, explains:

"Before observation, all possible conditions have a given probability; after observation, this uncertainty is removed, resulting in one choice. The observation is called the collapse of the state vector. Since this collapse cannot take place without an observer, physicists are now required to consider the role of consciousness in the process. ... We are left with a quantity called consciousness that appears to be involved in physics, but is non-physical and non-measurable."

According to 1984 Nobel Laureate Carlo Rubbia, matter is less than a billionth part of the manifest universe. The rest is pure energy phenomena of interactions, information fields and resonance. Information fields put things where they are and hold them there. Everything is basically just information, which materializes when we interact with it.

In the Zero Point Field, particles and waves spontaneously pop into and out of existence with a randomness that cannot be predicted by science. The zero-point fluctuations were originally traced to the Uncertainty Principle, the emissions being considered "spontaneous" because they could not be predicted ahead of time. However, what had been thought to be a spontaneous emission now appears to be a "stimulated emission," induced by the zero-point fluctuations in the field.

The question is then, "What stimulates these fluctuations?" Modern information theory links them to consciousness, which "informs," or gives form to, reality. British physician Dr Keith Scott-Mumby suggests in his 1999 book *Virtual Medicine* that information fields, or quantum probability fields, are the intermediate domain between consciousness and reality made manifest. He observes:

"[I]nformation implies consciousness of a sort. ... The word information means to give material form to (from the Latin *informare*). In other words, information at the quantum field level is actually an active, creative force intimately involved in the form and manifestation of reality. Stated differently, information is a specific way of representing the interaction of consciousness and reality, either as a means of organizing it or decoding it."

Consciousness, it seems, gives form to reality rather than the reverse. In this model, all kinds of possibilities arise and there is suddenly room for serious consideration of the effects of prayer on health and well-being, long-distance healings, and psychic phenomena of all kinds.

David Bohm - An Alternative View

David Bohm (1917-1992), a Nobel Prize winner and one of the most distinguished scientists of his generation, had a view contrary to conventional quantum theory, although his theory led to similar conclusions as those discussed above. Bohm had difficulty accepting that subatomic particles took on definite properties only when observed and that the quantum world was characterised by indeterminism and chance. He developed two radical scientific theories: the causal interpretation of quantum physics and the theory of the implicate order and undivided wholeness. In his view, subatomic particles such as electrons are not simple, structure less particles, but highly complex, dynamic entities. In addition, their motion is not uncertain or ambiguous, but follows a specific path. This path is determined not only by conventional physical forces, but also by a more subtle force that he calls the "quantum potential." This quantum potential pervades all space and provides direct connections between quantum systems. It is able to guide the motion of particles by providing "active information" about the whole environment.

Bohm also suggested that the quantum potential corresponds to implicate order. In his view, all the separate objects, entities, structures, and events in the visible or explicable world around us are relatively autonomous, stable and temporary "sub-totalities" derived from a deeper, implicative order of unbroken wholeness. Furthermore, the quantum potential itself is organized by a super-quantum potential, representing a second implicate order, and on ad infinitum. There may be an infinite number of implicate orders, and Bohm believed that all life and consciousness are enfolded deep within this order and are, therefore, present in varying degrees of enfoldment in all matter, including "inanimate" matter such as electrons and plasmas. The mystical connotations of Bohm's ideas are highlighted by his remark that the implicate domain "could equally be called Idealism, Spirit, Consciousness. The separation of the two—matter and spirit—is an abstraction."

Chapter 3
Beyond the Illusion of Space and Time

"[A]t the sub quantum level, the level in which the quantum potential operated, location ceased to exist. All points in space became equal to all other points in space, and it was meaningless to speak of anything as being separate from anything else. Physicists call this property 'nonlocality.' "

– Michael Talbot, *The Holographic Universe*

The British researcher Rupert Sheldrake has also conducted experiments that suggest that instantaneous transfer of energy over a distance is possible. Sheldrake has shown through extensive double-blind studies that dogs are capable of determining by extrasensory perception (ESP) when their masters are coming home. The phenomenon of ESP, says Sheldrake, demonstrates that a field like electromagnetism or gravity joins consciousnesses, human and non-human. He calls it a "morphogenetic field," or "M-Field."

M-Fields are invisible organizing patterns that act as energy templates to establish the forms of the various kinds of life. In a phenomenon termed "formative causation," once an M-Field is created, it is picked up and reinforced by other minds, creating a stronger and stronger thought pattern. Sheldrake writes:

"When Roger Bannister broke the four-minute mile, he created a new M-Field. The belief system prevailing in human consciousness had been that the four-minute mile was the limit of human possibility. Once the new M-Field was created, many runners suddenly began to run sub-four-minute miles. ... Once an M-Field is created, everyone who repeats the accomplishment reinforces the power of that M-Field. ... It is a standing energy field which is everywhere present."

The phenomenon has been found to be true not just for humans, but also for animals ("the hundredth monkey phenomenon"). It is seen, for example, in rats learning to negotiate a maze. It takes time for rats to learn the route of a new maze. Nevertheless, laboratory records show that once the initial group of rats has learned the route, other rats new to the same maze will run it with unexplained ease. What is even more unusual is that rats in other labs across the world seem to learn the maze more quickly, too. Rats thereafter apparently learn the maze by some process of communication independent of physical contact, interaction or distance.

Remarkably, the principle of formative causation has been observed even at the molecular level. This is seen in a class of substances known as "organic crystals." When the mother liquid from which they crystallize is allowed to stand, it can often take an hour or more for the first crystals to appear. However, when the process is repeated under identical circumstances, the time needed for crystallization rapidly decreases, until researchers around the world are routinely producing them within a few minutes of preparation.

How is that possible? If crystals can learn to grow faster because other crystals have "shown the way," they must be plugged into some sort of collective field by which they can communicate with other crystals; an information field that is not dependent on individual human minds and is outside of time and space.

A morphogenetic field is outside time and space because it lacks energy; it therefore does not diminish with distance, as do various forms of energy. It is an information field: it contains the detail needed to create form but lacks the energy to manifest it (morpho = form; genesis = giving birth to).

In his book *Virtual Medicine*, Dr Keith Scott-Mumby reports on a conference he attended in 1995 in St. Petersburg, where leading Russian scientists lectured on a model that would explain psychic phenomena. The model involved "torsion fields" that are outside time and space. Writes Dr. Scott-Mumby:

"Matter, we now know, has three basic properties: charge, mass and spin. Each of these gives rise to a characteristic field. Charge creates an electromagnetic field, mass gives rise to a gravitational field, and spin generates what we call a torsion field. ... [T]orsion fields are different in having instantaneous effects at all points. Gravity fields have a distance effect, and electromagnetic propagation has a time (frequency) effect. ... Torsion fields, almost by definition, have neither a distance nor a time effect. In other words, we were hearing about a model which could explain telepathy and other supposedly etheric phenomena, which are so often dismissed as totally implausible."

Negative Entropy and the Etheric Plane

Dr. William Tiller explains psychic or etheric phenomena in terms of "negative space/time." Dr Tiller used Einstein's equation relating energy to matter to predict the existence of the etheric plane. Richard Gerber, M.D., explains Dr Tiller's thesis in his classic book *Vibrational Medicine*:

"Up until now most physicists have accepted the seeming limitation that one cannot accelerate matter beyond the speed of light. This assumption is partly related to the fact that when one inserts numbers greater than the speed of light into the Einstein-Lorenz Transformation, one arrives at solutions containing the square root of -1, which is considered an imaginary number. Since most physicists do not believe in imaginary numbers, they assume that the speed of light is the maximum velocity at which matter can travel."

Yet, notes Dr Gerber, physicists with impunity use these imaginary numbers every day. They are necessary to finding solutions to the equations of electromagnetic theory and quantum theory. Physicists have proposed the existence of a particle known as a "tachyon," which would theoretically exist only at speeds exceeding the speed of light. Dr Tiller hypothesized that the realm of negative square roots, or "negative space/time," predicted by Einstein's equation is the etheric plane. In negative space/time, particles move faster than the speed of light and have negative mass. Positive space/time matter is associated with the forces of electricity and electromagnetic radiation. Negative space/time matter is linked to magnetism and what Dr Tiller calls magneto-electric radiation. Positive space/time matter is characterized by positive entropy: it runs down and becomes less organized over time. Negative space/time matter is characterized by negative entropy: it becomes *more* organized over time.

The most notable exception to the rule of entropy in the physical universe, according to Dr Gerber, is found in living systems. They take in raw materials and energy that are less organized and build them into systems that are more organized. The life forces that do this building in human beings emanate from the etheric and astral bodies existing in negative space/time. In the body, negative entropy (structure and organization) is equated with health. Entropy—the tendency of cells to go back to their independent, disorganized state—is equated with disease.

The Human Energy Field

The principles of field physics have been used to develop an "electrodynamic theory of life." This theory has grown out of research showing that living matter is surrounded and controlled by electrodynamic fields; that electrical forces are inherent in all living systems and are important determinants of their organization; and that disease states are accompanied by consistent changes in the electrical conductivity of individual tissue cells.

Orthopaedic surgeon Robert O. Becker, a pioneer in the field of bioelectric science, has demonstrated that the body has a DC electric field. He has also shown that general anaesthesia leads to a complete attenuation of that field. Consciousness, it seems, is not in the grey matter but in the nonlocal field surrounding it.

The human energy field however, does not consist merely of electrical phenomena. Kirlian photography validates the existence of a more subtle field corresponding to the "aura" popularized in New Age literature. At the University of California at Los Angeles, Professor Emeritus Dr Valerie Hunt has spent more than two decades probing the human energy field and its relationship to health and disease. She has explored the use of Kirlian photography, computers, oscilloscopes, chaos theory and film from a regular camera enhanced with the aid of a computer that runs amber light through it, making the field around the body visible. Applying cross-plot analysis to graphs recorded by oscilloscope of myograms of muscle contractions, Dr Hunt found that all living things have a "chaos pattern," and that "anti-coherency patterns" result in various physical disabilities, including cardiac arrhythmia.

She also found something astounding in its implications: both disease and healing enter the energetic field *before* they enter the body. She wrote, "We discovered by recording brain waves, blood pressure changes, galvanic skin responses, heartbeat and muscle contraction simultaneously with auric changes that changes occurred in the field before any of the other systems changed."

The phenomenon of Multiple Personality Disorder (MPD) demonstrates that health and disease exist at the level of consciousness and can be affected there. Many cases are on record in which a person with MPD has manifested different functional disease states depending on the personality in control. Under one personality, the body will have high blood pressure; under another personality, the same body will have normal blood pressure. The body under one personality will be allergic to cats; under another personality, cats can be petted without reaction. It seems that health and disease are not set in concrete in the genes but fluctuate according to the thought and emotional patterns that make up the personality.

These findings validate what Eastern religion and Eastern medicine have declared for centuries—that disease occurs first in the energy matrix of the subtle bodies underlying the physical body. Disorganization in the energy matrix of the subtle bodies is the cause of disease; and this disorganization can be balanced with subtle energies, augmenting wellness.

Chapter 4
Holograms, Interference Fields and Subtle Energy Bodies

"If you want to understand life, don't think about vibrant, throbbing gels and oozes, think about information technology."

– Richard Dawkins, *The Blind Watchmaker*, 1986

Other research suggests that the body functions like a hologram. Disease results when the vibrational rate of a distress pattern in the body's field is slower than that of the underlying biological hum of the body. Information theory holds that the universe itself, despite its apparent solidity, is actually a hologram. Like the illusory holographic figures dancing in the Haunted House at Disneyland, it consists simply of interference fields generated by overlapping patterns of light.

Physicists create holographic phenomena using a single frequency of coherent or polarized light. A hologram results when the wave pattern generated by a split beam of light is disrupted by an interference field. A three-dimensional image is produced by splitting a laser beam into two beams, a reference beam and an object beam. The reference beam, which is direct and unsplit, lays down a background field of photons. A mirror splits the object beam. When it collides with the reference beam, an interference pattern is created in the background field. The result is a hologram that exactly duplicates the object copied.

A hologram differs from an ordinary photograph in that any tiny piece of it contains the whole. If you cut up a regular photograph of an apple, you get a jigsaw puzzle of independent pieces—stem, leaf, sections of the apple, etc. However, cut up a hologram of an apple and you get many small, but whole apples. Although each apple will not be as clear as the original because each copy contains less light (or information), each "piece" of a hologram accesses the whole information field of the subject.

The Hologram of the Body

The elements of a hologram are contained in the human body. A recent Swedish study established that a standing frequency, or biological hum, is continuously present in the body. It is a generated frequency that is secondary to all body-system functioning and it generates a sine wave (a snake-like wave). If the background hum of the body is the reference wave and a diseased or disharmonious structure is creating interference, the elements of a hologram are produced. The disturbance field has a different frequency, a distressed or stressed frequency. These two beams—the background sine wave generated by the body and the disturbance field distorting that wave in a particular area—creates an interference field that can be detected clinically.

The blood also has holographic qualities. Like light, it has both wave and particle properties. It is both a fluid and a collection of solid cells. The blood is the ocean of the body; and because it is a fluid, it is a very good conductor of signals. The blood, which is among the most complex aspects of the body, is the body's information highway, carrying the immune system and information for a wide array of biochemical reactions.

It has also been suggested that the brain may have holographic properties because of the distributed nature of its functions: for example, a specific memory is not located in one area or structure of the brain, but appears to be distributed throughout it. Damage to one aspect of the brain may not mean the loss of the function associated with that structure, as other parts of the brain are elastic enough to compensate. The brain has even been shown to generate stem cells (precursor cells that, basically, can become any other type of cell) that migrate to damaged areas when directed by a biofeedback-type signal generated by the damaged part.

The Emotional Basis of the Interference Fields Causing Disease

Rudolf Steiner, a German researcher writing early in the twentieth century, used a form of psychic cognition to explore the interplay of subtle energy fields causing disease in the body. Steiner's insights reflect the holographic model. While not yet proven scientifically, they are provocative, potentially filling in gaps in current theories of life and how it behaves.

Steiner developed a philosophy called anthroposophy, which looks at the world in terms of man's spiritual nature. It is based on a form of psychic awareness Steiner maintained was accessible to anyone with proper training. Anthroposophical medicine is based on his teachings and is practiced by medically qualified doctors who have undergone special training. Steiner reported that we have not one but four bodies: the physical body, the etheric body (vital but unconscious bodily forces), the astral body or soul (feelings and emotions), and the ego or spirit (mind and thought). The etheric, or vital body, we possess in common with the world of plants. The astral body we possess in common with animals. The ego or spirit is unique to man. Disease is a disturbance in the equilibrium of those bodies. Healing comes when balance is restored.

The vital body is the "aura" seen in Kirlian photography. Steiner proposed that it provides the formative forces active in the human embryo. Substantial research now establishes that plant and animal bodies and organs form templates or patterns in some form of invisible etheric medium and that these templates persist even when parts of the plant or animal body are excised. Many holistic medical sciences, including homeopathy, acupuncture, osteopathy, chiropractic and naturopathy, are based on the premise that an underlying pattern or template of energy feeds and sustains the body and all its organs, and that disease occurs when and where that energy pattern is impaired.

Steiner observed that "disease" implies the ability to self-heal. Only things with the ability to heal are said to get sick. A rock can get broken, but it cannot get diseased because it cannot regenerate itself into wholeness. The ability to heal or regenerate comes from the vital body. Plants, which have a vital body, can heal themselves. In fact, under most circumstances, they can heal themselves better than higher animals can. Plants and primitive animals have the ability to regenerate themselves completely. If you pluck a leaf from a tree, it will grow another. If you chop a limb from a salamander, it will grow another. Kirlian photography reveals that the new appendage grows according to a template or pattern in the vital body.

Kirlian photography also reveals that higher animals and humans have etheric templates; but when higher animals and humans lose a limb, they cannot regrow it. The reason, says Steiner, is that the astral body intervenes. The etheric body of a plant is essentially independent of the physical body, which regrows strictly according to the etheric body's patterns. The etheric body of a human becomes glued to the physical body by means of the astral body, which causes the etheric body to become "injured" along with the physical body.

The vital body vibrates at a higher rate when it is unhindered than when it is in the "field" of an astral body slowed by contracting emotions. The hardening of the etheric template Steiner called "etheric crystallization." Crystals grow in a certain pattern, like a snowflake. In this interplay of energy fields, the body is functioning like a hologram: a holographic pattern results because the vibrational rate of the distress pattern is slower than that of the "reference beam," the underlying biological hum of the body.

Chapter 5
Detecting and Affecting the Human Energy Field

"It is theory that decides what we can observe."

– Albert Einstein

Homeopathy

Homeopathy is a later medical system in which health is thought to be evoked on an energetic level. In this it differs from conventional medicine, which works chemically. Homeopathic remedies are "succussed," or shaken vigorously with each dilution, to increase their vibratory field. They are thought to work by stimulating the body's own healing energy, rather like a tuning fork that sets disharmonious chords back on track.

Homeopathic remedies consist of minute doses of natural substances—mineral, plant or animal—that if given to healthy people in larger doses would cause the symptoms the patient is experiencing. The principle is similar to that of pharmaceutical vaccination, but vaccines are macromolecules that can induce unwanted side effects. Homeopathic remedies are without side effects (but not reactions) because they are extremely dilute—at some strengths they are so dilute that no molecule of the original substance is likely to be left in solution. It is thought that only the original substance's vibration remains. While this explanation strains the credulity of conventional medicine, studies have indicated that some of the effects of homeopathy cannot be attributed solely to the placebo effect.

Electrodermal Screening Devices

Disturbance fields in the body are documented and interpreted clinically using a number of tests and tools. Besides Kirlian photography, which picks up disturbances in the electromagnetic field generated by the body, these tools include thermography, which measures disturbances in the heat patterns of the body; and electrodermal screening devices, which detect interference fields of the body.

Reinhold Voll, M.D., created one of the first devices for measuring and harmonizing the body's electrical patterns in the 1950s. Dr Voll was a former professor of neuroanatomy who developed a system called ElectroAcupuncture by Voll (EAV) to test the different electrical points of the body. Using his device, he confirmed the existence and location of acupuncture meridians, or patterns of energy flow, that had been mapped in the body by the Chinese thousands of years ago.

Dr Voll used his EAV machine to locate interference fields that impaired the functioning of the body by preventing the necessary electromagnetic signals from getting through. He was particularly interested in the teeth, a central transmitting station through which the meridians of all the major organ systems passed. Dr Voll and a dentist colleague located and mapped an electromagnetic connection between specific organs, muscles, joints and tissues and every tooth. They found, for example, that the top incisor teeth are connected energetically to the urogenital area; the bottom incisor teeth are connected to the bladder; and the wisdom teeth are connected to the nervous system and heart. Dr Voll estimated that 80 percent of the body's energy blockages arise in the teeth and jaw.

More recent modifications of the Voll machine are becoming increasingly popular diagnostic tools in various health fields. These electrodermal screening devices are used for determining which remedies the patient needs and which materials are compatible with the body. Proponents say the devices can tell the type and degree of dysfunction in particular organs, along with causes and potential cures.

Many researchers have verified that the skin's electrical potential is more positive at acupuncture points than in the surrounding tissue. The conductivity of acupuncture points on the heart meridian increases as heart rate is increased by biofeedback, while the conductivity of normal skin nearby does not change. One of the theories behind electrodermal screening devices is that the machine is able to measure the energy flowing through particular acupuncture points, which are connected to acupuncture meridians running to various organs of the body. When the meridians are in balance, the needle registers somewhere around 50 on a scale of 0 to 100 and when the needle drops too low or soars too high, the meridian is out of balance. The correct remedy, placed on a plate attached electronically to the indicator touching the acupuncture points, will bring the needle back to 50.

Disease processes have been shown to begin with a change in the electrical potential of the skin. Practitioners say electrodermal screening in the disease's initial stages can identify this change, when the patient is still unaware of any sensations and conventional diagnosis produces no definitive results. Electrodermal screening can establish an immediate case report, without a prior patient history, based entirely on measurement readings. The machines can also tell which remedies will resonate harmonically to correct electromagnetic imbalances in the body.

European researchers following Voll reasoned that to heal itself, the human body system was looking not for chemicals or drugs but for new or lost information. They succeeded in building instruments that could read part of the patient's body-field, detect imbalances, and feed a corrective signal (information) back to the patient's body-field. They found that pathogens resonating at specific frequencies could be destroyed by increasing their resonant frequency amplitude, in the same way that a high-intensity pitch can shatter glass. Using similar principles, healthy tissues could be enhanced or amplified.

The idea that everything has its own unique vibration or signature (described later by NES as a set of magnetic vectors) is actually an ancient one, dating back to Pythagoras in the sixth century B.C. The Pythagoreans were the most learned men of their time, possessing all the sciences known including geometry, astronomy, physics, music and medicine. Pythagoras determined the relation between the length of a string and the tune it produces when struck, leading to the discovery of the musical scale and advances in mathematics. The Pythagoreans reduced everything to number, which was conceived as the principle and innermost essence of the various manifestations of Universal Mind. They conceived a sort of atomic theory by which material phenomena were considered crystallizations of vibrations represented by numbers. Every object or being was thought to represent a number of universal force vibrations, acting upon human consciousness similar to the way in which suggestion acts in hypnotism. Healing was effected through Universal Mind by a form of hypnotic suggestion at the level of consciousness.

Using Instruments to Read and Balance the Body's Energy Field

Homeopathic medicines transfer healing energies through water or sugar pills, but this transfer can also be affected through devices that work with quantum electrodynamic (QED) fields. Locating and correcting distortions in the body's energy field can be done using instrumentation that detects or broadcasts QED fields.

In the twentieth century, the first instrument used to measure distortions in the body's subtle energy patterns was the pendulum. But long before that, traditional African healers were rubbing two sticks together and getting readings from when they "stuck." A French priest named Abbe Mermet devised a system called "medical dowsing". He got the idea from the mysterious dowsing technique used to locate water hidden underground. Mermet reasoned that if he could detect the condition of an underground stream with a pendulum, he might also be able to detect the condition of the human body with it. He practiced the technique on hospital patients to whom he had access as a priest. His technique came to be called "radiesthesia" (sensing rays).

The next refinement in the field was the "Abrams box." Albert Abrams, M.D., was a celebrated American neurologist who did his research at Stanford University early in the twentieth century. In 1919, Abrams devised a machine that could emit signals at variable frequencies that were capable of cancelling out "radiations" emitted by various diseases. The machine effectively duplicated and took the place of homeopathic remedies. In 1924, the British medical establishment set up a blue-ribbon committee to investigate the Abrams technique. The committee, headed by Sir Thomas Horder (later Lord Horder, the Queen's physician), intended to discredit the practice in England before it caught on. The committee examined a variant of the Abrams box called an emanometer, operated by a Scottish homeopath named W. E. Boyd. Under scrupulously controlled conditions that eliminated the possibility of fraud, Boyd had to distinguish between apparently identical substances in identical bottles, secretly marked. To the shock and dismay of the committee, he was nearly 100 percent accurate in these tests. Sir Thomas told the Royal Society of Medicine that the odds of this happening by chance were millions to one.

The American leader in the field that Abrams had pioneered was Ruth Drown, a chiropractor who devised her own bio-energetic equipment and was highly proficient at operating it. In 1951, she too was investigated for fraud and in her case, the verdict was guilty; but it was highly controversial. Edward Russell, a British writer, gave this account of her trial by an eyewitness:

"[M]any in the court had formed the impression that the charge against her was trumped up. Efforts to have her patients testify that her treatment was ineffective were a complete failure. All the patients testified to her correct diagnosis and treatment. ... One after another—very real and healthy people—testified that they had been cured of all kinds of diseases and ailments. ... When the jury went out, the court stenographer was certain she would be acquitted. To everyone's surprise, she was not. The best guess as to why, was that the jury were more impressed by the radio experts who testified that the instruments could not work as a radio."

Like with many innovators before and since, Dr Drown was defeated because science had no explanation for her work. The modern explanation is that she was working with something

47

more subtle than radio waves, an underlying field beyond time or space that connects us all.

Beyond the Placebo Effect: Devices that Work on Plants and Metals

Detection of a disease or illness from afar and healing at a distance has been achieved not only with human beings but also with plants and metals. In England in the 1940s, a civil engineer named George de la Warr designed a machine known as the "black box." Among other experiments conducted by him and his wife was one that involved focusing subtle energy through a lens system at diseased plants. They found they could affect the plants' growth not only by beaming energy directly at the plants, but also by focusing the machine on a photograph of the plants. Then they tried treating the soil by beaming radiations that were the vibratory equivalent of plant nutrients at it. They cleared two garden areas eighty feet apart and allowed the soil to settle, then photographed one of the sites and began a four-week treatment using the photograph in their machine. The other site was not treated. After the four-week treatment period, they planted cabbages in both plots. They reported that two months later the cabbages growing in the irradiated section were three times larger than those in the non-radiated section were.

This line of research was continued in the United States by another civil engineer, Curtis P. Upton, whose father had been a partner of Thomas Edison. Upton's interest was pest control. He aerial-photographed a field of cotton that was plagued by insect pests and the photograph was then placed on a plate in Upton's device along with a reagent known to be poisonous to the pests, a treatment considered the energetic equivalent of homeopathy. Remarkably, it was completely successful and a million-dollar crop was saved.

The next development in the field was the "Hieronymus Machine." Modelled after the Abrams box, it was built by T. Galen Hieronymus for the purpose of detecting energies emitted by metals. An article published by magazine editor John Campbell in the 1950s reported that the Hieronymus Machine could analyse the component elements of an ore sample without the aid of ordinary physical methods and could influence and even kill living organisms. Moreover, it could do this from vast distances with no scientifically understandable mechanism at the other end. Campbell was so intrigued that he obtained patents and built his own machine, which he became convinced could do everything claimed.

The most remarkable development in this line of inquiry was Campbell's discovery that if he drew the circuit diagram of the machine on a sheet of paper, using only India ink as a conductor, the circuit conductor worked as well as the machine itself. "Your electronic circuit," Campbell wrote to Hieronymus later, "represents a pattern of relationships. The electrical characteristics are unimportant and can be dropped out completely."

This result would have to be considered either magical or fraudulent under conventional theory. However, it becomes credible in the light of modern information theory and new discoveries concerning the human body-field.

Section B introduces current research in the field of quantum biology, which explains more scientifically how biological systems can be controlled and healed through the methods outlined in Section A. It also outlines our work on the NES theory of the human body-field.

Section C then describes how we have turned that theory into a comprehensive health assessment system.

Section B

Quantum Biology:
The First Map of the
Quantum Electrodynamic
Human Body-Field

Chapter 6
Introduction to Quantum Biology

"The Quantum Theory is, at present, the most basic way available in physics for understanding the fundamental and universal laws relating to matter and its movement. As such, it must clearly be given serious consideration in any attempt to develop an overall world view."

– David Bohm, *The Undivided Universe*

Although quantum theory has been at the heart of many branches of science since its discovery in the early twentieth century—and despite the fact that quantum underlies all of chemistry—it was not until very recently that biologists began to search for quantum processes in the body.

There are many biological phenomena that cannot be explained by the current biochemical and physical models of how living organisms function. For instance, there is no convincing explanation for the precise synchrony of motion that occurs in huge flocks of birds or schools of fish. In some types of fish, the entire school seems to be "one mind." They can sense the approach of a predator and take evasive action not as individuals but seamlessly as a huge group. Alternatively, they can spontaneously form a large "ball" to ward off the prey. If the group does scatter then, once the danger passes the individuals effortlessly and almost instantaneously reform into a group. Known forms of communication, such as sight or sound, cannot explain this simultaneity of behaviour. It seems as if the fish possess a "sixth sense" that is guiding their movements. Could a quantum description of biology help to explain this behaviour?

Large flocks of birds act in a similar, unexplainable fashion. It is not uncommon for a flock to grow to as many as 100,000 birds and yet the flock is still able to change direction almost instantaneously. Flocks are also able to navigate over extremely long distances to return to exact locations repeatedly, year after year. There does not appear to be a constant "leader" in a flock, showing the direction of travel to the rest of the group.

Another, more extreme example of coordinated behaviour is that of thousands of male fireflies switching their lights on and off in unison. While a flock of birds will move generally in the same direction, the individual birds will match wing beats only for a few measures. Similarly, horses that are harnessed together will act as a unit, but they normally will not match their steps perfectly one horse to the next. Only a few creatures show precise synchrony between individuals in the group: certain chorusing insects like crickets and katydids, and the flashing of some species of firefly. These firefly species are not only able to flash in time as a large group but they also seem to be able, individually, to adjust the time between flashes to provide for that perfect synchrony. This phenomenon is said to have something to do with mating, as it is only the males that perform this ritual. However, current observers of fireflies cannot explain how the insects achieve these impressive displays of synchronization.

There is a growing amount of mathematical research into the area of coordinated behaviour that concentrates on modelling the motions of individuals in a large group (e.g., birds in a flock) by a series of rules. In a number of cases, programmers have been able to encode the rules for the individual actions into a computer and receive output that simulates the observed coordinated group action. By extrapolation, mathematicians suggest that flock behaviour can be explained by formulating simple rules for the individual birds, such as "don't get too close to any other bird" or "stay within a certain angle of another bird." However, these models cannot explain why and how flocks form in the first place, and how they reach specific destinations. Does one bird suddenly decide to form a flock and other birds join it? Or is there some sort of collective action at a precise point in time? How is the final destination decided upon and how is it navigated toward? Therefore, although these computer models are helpful in explaining how these actions might be carried out, they are unable to explain why these biological phenomena occur in the first place.

Current biological theory is also far from clear about the how and why of basic human body functions. For example, it cannot yet explain how the human body functions as a heat-generating object. Cold-blooded species seem to obey the Second Law of Thermodynamics, but warm-blooded species do not. Heat is supposed to dissipate according to certain rules and maintaining body heat to within 1 degree Celsius is no mean feat, especially considering the number of cells in the body and the wide range of external temperatures to which the human body is subjected.

The current explanation of how the human nervous system functions is also not particularly satisfactory. The current thinking is that nerves are like on/off switches and neurons act as wires connecting them. Therefore, the brain can be likened to a computer. However, if the nervous system was concerned only with ions and the transmission of electrochemical signals, surely it would have been designed as a continuous unit. Instead, the nervous system is discontinuous, rather like a collection of fine fibres spreading throughout the body.

There has been much research involving the close examination of these fibres and attempting to link pathways through the fibres to regions of the brain. The nervous system, it is suggested, must work via neural transmission at different speeds, varying from fast to slow in a way that is related to the diameter of the controlling axon. However, this would make any action almost impossible to coordinate. Anyone who has watched a ballet dancer or an Olympic gymnast observes that such activities require high levels of precision. Could a number of on/off switches really control this level of pinpoint precision? Or would the discontinuous nature of the nervous system be better described in terms of a quantum system that is able to transfer information instantaneously via fields? If the structures of the brain—their cavities, orientations and placement with regards to fluids—are considered alongside the charges that are set up by the nervous system, it is quite easy to see that all of the elements required to set up a complex field system for transferring information are present.

These examples, and numerous others, lead to the conclusion that the current way of viewing living organisms is not completely satisfactory and that a more unifying approach is required. Many of the ideas discussed in the previous chapters though—such as Sheldrake's morphogenetic fields, Tiller's directed intent and various bio resonance devices—are not warmly regarded by the current medical profession. According to Peter Fraser, an independent Australian researcher, this is in part due to the difficulty in explaining natural therapy and alternative ideas in the language used by conventional science and medicine. He says that there is a gulf between the two disciplines that is difficult to cross because of the lack of shared terminology. In the following pages, we will investigate the work of a number of researchers who have attempted to bridge this gap.

Nonlocal Information Transfer

For many of the phenomena we have discussed in Section A and in the above examples from the natural world to be possible, instantaneous communication at a distance must take place. A great deal of recent work in physics has shown that this "nonlocal" communication is possible. Simply put, "nonlocal" means that information can somehow be transmitted across space and time, without any known mechanism because it must happen faster than the speed of light, which is supposed to be the upper limit of motion.

The question of faster-than-light communication really began to be answered when Einstein questioned the fundamental principles of quantum theory in the 1930s. He believed that the quantum theory developed by Bohr and others, now the accepted way of viewing quantum theory, was incomplete and would be improved upon in the future. In 1935, along with Boris Podolsky and Nathan Rosen, Einstein proposed a thought experiment that became known as the EPR paradox (after the initials of the three scientists). We will not explain the thought experiment here, but suffice to say, it caught the attention of many scientists, who attempted to prove that "action at a distance" (nonlocality) was either possible or not.

In 1982, a remarkable experiment was performed in Paris by a research team led by physicist Alain Aspect. This ingenious experiment, based on the EPR paradox and an inequality principle derived by John Bell, was the first to "prove" the principle of quantum entanglement. Quantum entanglement is a property that allows two particles to behave as one, no matter how far apart they are. The results of Aspect's experiment clearly showed that subatomic particles once coupled and then separated are still connected at some fundamental level. Researchers in Austria, led by Marcus Aspelmeyer, carried out a more recent experiment into quantum entanglement, reported in the June 2003 edition of *New Scientist*. They successfully sent entangled photons to opposite sides of the Danube River without the use of optical fibres. Every year more scientific evidence appears supporting the theory of the quantum interconnectedness of the universe.

David Bohm and his research student, Yakir Aharonov, performed an experiment back in 1959 that supported this view. Now described as the Bohm-Aharonov (AB) effect, they found that in certain circumstances electrons are able to "feel" the presence of a nearby magnetic field, even though they are travelling in regions of space where the field strength is zero. This example of quantum interconnectedness and others led Bohm to develop his theories regarding implicate order in the world of matter and, by extension, in biological systems.

Biophotons

Biophotons are human cells that emit light. Professor Fritz-Albert Popp, vice president of the International Institute of Biophysics, is a pioneer in biophotonic research and experimentally verified this phenomenon in the early 1970s.

In 1976, Popp and Ruth developed very sensitive experimental equipment that could measure low levels of light emission in the human body and other living organisms. They showed evidence of weak, but permanent, light emission in the visible range (400–800 nm) from plant and animal cells and tissues. They coined the term "biophotons" to express the biological origins and the quantum character of this radiation. Since this discovery, sound experimental evidence has been published to show that DNA is one of the sources of biophotons, and that there is structure to the biophotonic field. In addition, there is evidence to support the idea that biophotons are responsible for triggering some biochemical reactions in and between cells. The Popp research group has also recorded biophoton measurements from the whole human body over a period of many months. These measurements reveal that the biophoton field reflects all the biological rhythms as well as left–right symmetry of corresponding points on the body in healthy people.

Cyril W. Smith, a British biomedical engineer and physicist, has been conducting experiments in this area since the early 1970s. His background as a senior lecturer in electronics and electrical engineering led him to develop radiaesthetic techniques, specifically to investigate "subtle" electromagnetic fields and radiations. Since 1973, he has led studies of the interaction of coherent electromagnetic fields with living systems and biological materials. He concludes that living systems produce a characteristic pattern of frequencies as an expression of their electrochemical activities. These frequencies are strong enough to induce observable synchronization in tadpoles in the presence of yellow light. Smith is proposing bio communication between organisms in the presence of light and a weak electromagnetic field. He suggests that this unseen information transfer is accomplished by the macroscopic systems relying on photon exchange in the presence of magnetic vector potentials. His theory has clear links to Popp's concept of biophotons.

Biological Superconducting Pathways

Matti Pitkanen, a Finnish theoretical physicist, has proposed that many principles of quantum physics can be applied to biological systems. He suggests that information transfer in biology takes place via a superconductive pathway and that electrons and photons are the carriers of this information. This work was supported by experiments performed by Freeman W. Cope in the 1970s. Cope produced pivotal work linking physics and biology and developed a solid-state theory of biological processes. He deduced that the activity in the cell is not just electrochemical. He also looked at the cell function as if the organelles were three-dimensional semi-conductors. His theory suggests that all the structures within the cell can be considered to be in a field in which there is constant interaction between all subatomic particles, not just between the charges on electrons. Cope published a paper in 1978 showing that hydrated nucleic acids or dry melanin produce low-frequency sound in measurements of electrical conductivity when exposed to magnetic fields at room temperature. From this he concluded that superconductivity, analogous to superconductivity in metals at very low temperatures, was occurring in living systems in the presence of a magnetic field. His overall view was that superconductive pathways play a controlling role in biological functions.

A New Model of Biology

These researchers, and those in previous chapters, seem to be thinking along the same lines: that there is some function, field, or energy controlling the biological systems other than, or in addition to, the biochemical and physical systems. After nearly thirty years of research, Peter Fraser now proposes an advanced model to explain the physiological phenomena of the human body based upon a QED body-field, which is measurable. The Fraser model unites a number of the concepts previously discussed with others from traditional biology. His theory is, in fact, a bridge between biology and physics and it is outlined in the remainder of this book.

Chapter 7
Mapping the Human Body-Field

"You cannot say A is made of B or vice versa. All mass is interaction."

– Richard Feynman, Nobel Laureate

Most of the general public views physics, biology and traditional medicine as separate disciplines with little, if any, interaction. It is clear however, that there must be links between these areas at a functional level. This concept is elaborated on in the radical Body-Field theory that Peter Fraser proposes. In order to understand the complex ideas that Fraser is introducing, it is first necessary to summarize the background and development of the technology that led to this groundbreaking work.

Background to Fraser's work

The Human Body-Field theory has its roots in complementary medical techniques. Fraser has devoted much of his life to studying these diverse practices and is convinced that they can be united and explained in a more scientific fashion than is currently presented.

The first system of complementary medicine that must be considered is Traditional Chinese Medicine (TCM). The traditional acupuncture system emerged in China some 2500 to 3000 years ago. The theory of this medical system is explained in an ancient text called *The Yellow Emperor's Classic of Internal Medicine*, which, despite its age, is still used in tertiary institutions. However, when we look for a satisfactory scientific explanation of acupuncture, we draw a blank. Traditional medicine for the most part does not accept "energy pathways" in the body. However, despite mainstream medicine's general scepticism, certain aspects of acupuncture have recently made their way into the fringes of conventional medicine. For example, acupunctural anaesthesia is well documented and is an accepted medical tool in many countries. The therapy consists of inserting slender needles into particular places in the muscular tissue of the body. The anaesthetic effect is measurable after twenty or more minutes of repeated, strong acupuncture stimulation.

How does it work? It has been discovered that acupunctural anaesthesia causes the release of endorphins in the brain. These are opium-like chemicals that are related to the perception of pain. This, at first glance, seems to be a satisfactory explanation until you ask how stimulating acupuncture points on the body can affect the brain. Is there a direct link between the points and the brain? If so, why can't anatomists find them in the body as actual physical structures? In another example, stimulation of an acupuncture point on the little toe causes the pituitary gland to release a hormone called oxytocin, which, among other benefits, relaxes the uterus during childbirth. There is no nerve linking the little toe with the pituitary gland or the uterus, so how can acupuncture achieve this result? Obviously, there are many questions about the "how" of acupuncture that are unanswerable. NES provides an explanation.

The second system we must consider is herbalism, which is used to good effect in most traditional cultures around the world. The third system is homeopathy, which we already discussed briefly. Homeopathy was developed in the eighteenth century in Germany by Dr Samuel Hahnemann and involves the serial dilution of herbs and minerals. Homeopathy and herbalism can be thought of as related as they both invoke the healing properties of substances found in the natural world. However, herbalism can be explained in a scientific context by simply analyzing the chemical components of a substance and then isolating the active "ingredients" that react with the chemical physiology of the body. In contrast, in homeopathy the active ingredients of the substance in question have been serially diluted so many times that, statistically speaking, there is very little probability that there is even one molecule left in the solution to physically interact with the body. The standard explanation in homeopathy is that the action of repeatedly shaking dilutions somehow "imprints" the information or vibration of the original substance in the homeopathic remedy. But what does this actually mean?

To begin to find answers, one has to venture into the realm of quantum theory. The origin of Fraser's research (more than 25 years ago) united TCM, homeopathy and quantum physics by describing the meridian system of TCM in terms of magnetic vectors. He was able to imprint magnetic vectors directly onto a set of ampoules to represent the different acupuncture meridians in the body and he was then able to relate these meridians to the overall human body-field. However, he has since discovered that the meridian system is only a small part of the overall body-field (details are explained later). Simply stated however, the result of his investigations showed that the body-field could be described in terms of a quantum electrodynamic (QED) field that is responsible for directing communication within biological systems.

Making History—Describing the Organization of the Human Body-Field

Fraser's initial findings were reported in the *Pacific Journal of Oriental Medicine*, but his research continued. He has spent years, from the start of his research program in the early 1980s to the present, carrying out tests that outline as clearly as possible the nature of the human body-field and its structure.

Fraser began by advancing the work of Dr H.S. Schimmel of Germany, who found out how to make energetic replicas of the Chinese acupuncture meridians. Schimmel made his replicas of the meridians simply by doing matches of the *materia medica* with those symptoms or aspects of the meridians that had found their way from China to the West. Moreover, he chose *materia medica* from the animal, vegetable and mineral kingdoms, so that each meridian analogue had three components. Overall, Schimmel made twelve analogues, with experimental use of *Ren Mai* and *Du Mai* as well.

Fraser, however, disputed the correctness of one of Schimmel's "meridian complexes," as they were called, because the Gall Bladder meridian was never satisfactory. Fraser decided to make an entirely new set of analogues from the *acupuncture points themselves*—and here the problem of what a meridian is and what an acupuncture point is became of primary importance. Over time, it became apparent to Fraser that the difference is that each point along a meridian will carry common information and it is the commonality of the information along various points that makes a meridian "pathway." The new meridian complexes Fraser prepared were never used commercially and were much like those of Schimmel, except over time they extended to 96 meridians, rather than to the original 12 that are the basis of the Traditional Chinese acupuncture system. Nobody wanted a system with 96 meridians. It was just too complicated to use in practice. Yet these formed the basis of Fraser's ongoing research into the structure of the human body-field.

Fraser discovered an especially curious aspect of the meridians that helped him to realise that there was *inner structure* to the acupuncture meridians: they appeared to be quantized. We can say "appeared to be" with good reason, for quantum mechanics is about the strange behaviour of subatomic particles and their odd ability to jump from one discrete energy level to another (each level or discrete "packet" of energy is a quanta). This jumping could never be attributed to something as ephemeral as a body-field system—unless the entire system depended on the motion of these various types of subatomic particles in a field.

The curious thing Fraser noted was that the meridian of the Small Intestine, when reduced to a set of magnetic vector information in an ampoule of alcohol, could be made to equate energetically with the Heart Meridian if two ampoules of Small Intestine Complex were used in the test. Anyone who has Schimmel's ampoules can do this simple test at home. Two ampoules of Small Intestine Complex will form a match with one ampoule of Heart Meridian Complex. And yes, the connections go on! Fraser found that three ampoules of Small Intestine Complex—of his own or of Helmut Schimmel's—would react with Spleen Meridian Complex. In fact, it turned out that all twelve of the Meridian Complexes could be arranged in order through this method of apparent quantization.

Fraser discovered there were two types of organization that could be shown experimentally: 1) the first meridian was a component of all the successive ones, and 2) this pattern of connection formed a sort of rational order of the meridians, an order that agreed with one of the orders of the meridians set out by the Chinese masters of acupuncture from the ancient texts.

Fraser used his findings to construct a theory explaining why it was that certain combinations of acupuncture points had specific effects on specific organs, effects that had previously been unexplained. In fact, he found that he could add or even subtract the numbers of the meridians to get certain predictable effects on other meridians. His theory, arrived at from these matching experiments, agreed with the theory of acupuncture as taught by some groups in China.

From Homeopathy to Isopathy

Still, for as much progress as he had made, Fraser was not happy with the way in which these meridian analogues worked, since theory predicted they should be a lot more powerful therapeutically than they turned out to be in practice. He, therefore, set out to take them a stage further. He wondered why everybody stopped at the idea of analogues when it would be possible to get equivalents of these body-field precursors from the body tissues themselves. So he ordered from a homeopathic supplier a full set of the cadaver body parts potentized in the correct fashion. There were hundreds of these and it took months to go through all of them and find out which tissue related to which meridian. His matching technique showed where "communication," for lack of a better term, occurred. The results were startling. Meridians when matched to body parts always returned the same results, that is, some were always and only related to myocardial tissues while other types matched only with the connective tissues in the body! Connective tissues are widely distributed throughout the body and it appeared from Fraser's experiments that many types of connective tissue all worked together to make a communication system in the body, although at that stage Fraser had no idea what sort of communication was taking place.

In effect, Fraser had turned the information from the body meridians of traditional acupuncture into isopathic "remedies." There were an immense number of them and they were never commercialized partly for that reason. Another reason is that it was difficult to get permits to use body tissues in remedies. Theoretically and experimentally however, Fraser had reached the point where he could now make a "picture" of the body-field from the actual parts of the body, instead of only from how some rare plant, heavy spice, or even mineral affected the body. Many more years of research passed during which Fraser used his knowledge of the body-field and his "remedies" as the basis of therapy while he was in practice in New South Wales. (A full report of his experiments was published in the *Pacific Journal of Oriental Medicine*.)

Despite all his research, Fraser still was not sure what a meridian actually was. He felt he was at an impasse in his research. Although he had been a teacher of acupuncture for thirteen years and was the President of the acupuncture college he founded in Melbourne, Australia, he had not the slightest idea what a meridian was, how it was formed, what it did, what type of energy it carried and even why we cannot see them. Fraser had openly admitted the lack of theoretical and experimental knowledge in his field, whereas his teachers and others had not for fear of retribution from both colleagues and students alike. In fact, Fraser had always denied the existence of bioenergy and even of *qi*, the mysterious energy that was supposed to flow in the so-called meridians that could be affected by the so-called points of acupuncture that obviously had correspondences with the vital energy of the homeopaths. As one of the pioneering acupuncture teachers in Australia, Fraser wrote an article saying, in effect, that there are only so many energy manifestations and these are known and described in detail by people called physicists. Their job is to express what happens in interactions of energy in terms of mathematics. Moreover, *qi* is not one of the energies the physicists write maths equations about, then or now. It was not that he did not believe in the existence of an unknown energy, but only that we should not have to resort to metaphysics to explain it. He believed there was a physical explanation.

But Fraser had no other way to talk about the meridians, and so he was forced to use this almost metaphysical language, such as the term *qi*. When Fraser met Professor Bevin Reid of NSW Australia, Reid immediately heaped scorn upon Fraser for his use of terminology that he called incomprehensible and fluffy - the very terminology Fraser had just spent thirteen years writing into a tertiary level acupuncture course opposed by every doctor in Australia and many academics. Yet Reid had a point and Fraser knew it. He became despondent and frustrated. He had spent many years doing something that he could never tell anyone about except therapists practising homeopathy and acupuncture. He knew that when we do not have "science," we have philosophy, which, he often joked, is what you make up when you cannot measure what you are talking about!

Reid was a maverick scientist, although he had gained repute in the field of magnetism and the links, such as they were at the time, between biology and physics. He has degrees in medicine and veterinary science and many years' post-graduate experience in oncology. A tempestuous and fretful man, he had scandalized many of his more conventionally minded colleagues with his increasingly dramatic, and some might say preposterous, experiments exploring action at a distance and other quantum phenomena as they relate to biology or physiology.

Although Reid had scoffed at Fraser's terminology, he was intensely interested in Fraser's work on the meridians. He generously financed Fraser's work for several years because he felt that Fraser was identifying underlying structures in the body-field and was formulating rules and even laws about how the field worked.

In a sense though, Fraser's brilliant career had crashed and his only solace was Reid, a far-out biological scientist, now retired. It was to turn out to be a fortuitous crash however, for Reid forever changed the face of what Fraser was doing.

Fraser did not give in to his frustration at wresting a viable theory from the evidence he had gathered about the relationship of meridians to the body-field. With renewed vigour, he plunged into new areas: revising his terminology, reading research papers in diverse fields, talking quantum physics with Reid for two hours on the phone every morning before breakfast, conducting new experiments, and reshaping his research effort so that, to put it bluntly, someone somewhere, besides he and Reid, would understand what he was doing.

From Isopathy to Physical Structures in Space

Fraser was looking for "The Control System" of the entire body which, when corrected, should not only deeply affect the way in which physiology functioned but make any correction permanent as well. If he was right in his thinking and testing, then the "remedies" he was making should work well. After all, they were preparations based on the body-field measurements and transformed by information based on how the cells of the body work.

But initially they did not work as well as expected. They worked better than traditional homeopathy, but did not often work with the spectacular ease the theory and experiments were indicating was possible. During ten years of work, from 1993 to 2003, Fraser cast his net of inquiry further afield as it became clear that something drastic needed to be done to make them work better. There had to be a piece missing from Fraser's theory of the body-field.

It was during this intense ten-year study that he came across "path integrals," complex sets of mathematics developed by the eminent physicist Richard Feynman, who had developed path integrals to explain where the electron might be found at any point in time. Fraser found this line of research especially interesting because it showed how to form patterns of apparent movement of subatomic particles in space. He also looked at unexplained phenomena in science such as sonoluminescence - a phenomenon that occurs when sound energy at a certain frequency injected into a certain fluid solution causes photons to be emitted. Fraser knew that body cells are bathed in fluid, that they emit photons regularly, and that a German doctor, Fritz-Albert Popp, has measured this "light". But in the end, he found that in physics there is no well-formed theory of how subatomic particles behave at low energy. There were only the rather prohibitive Uncertainty Principles by Bohr and Heisenberg that result in the "measurement problem," the conundrum of the wave-particle duality and how the wave function is collapsed so that one measures either a wave or a particle.

Fraser felt the wave-particle duality problem was, as Einstein and others had thought, a crack in quantum theory. In science, one often looks for cracks because that is where the theory may be incomplete and new information can be placed. Telltale signs of a gap in knowledge include the following:

Nobody wants to talk about it.

There is fuzzy theory surrounding it, like the Heisenberg Uncertainty and Copenhagen Interpretation of quantum.

There is mathematics that has no real resolution into clear constants: the Heisenberg theory lead to equations plagued by infinities, which is something that Feynman was concerned with and that drove him to develop his novel approaches to quantum mechanics and quantum electrodynamics.

Nobody knows how to measure the phenomenon accurately.

We also have to bear in mind that if your discovery is truly new, you will not find anything in the published literature about it because nobody has seen the problem and therefore nobody has sought an answer to it.

So what, Fraser asked, is the problem? We have apparent "preferred" pathways of subatomic particles in space in the virtual realm that may carry important information in biology and nobody has learned how to describe them or to measure them. In fact, although no textbook wants to talk about the *structure* of the electron (it is merely a charged particle), no textbook says it is not possible for it to have a structure in the real particle or in its virtual manifestation.

In 2002, while all this was percolating in Fraser's brain, he met Harry Massey. Fraser was doing some good soft shoe work trying to get some support for his formulation of the "map" of the body-field from Harry Massey, who himself had spent a lot of time trying to come to grips with space theory in physics and the realm of the virtual. During his discussions with Massey, Fraser had an insight - perhaps the biggest one of his life: he realized that he could measure physics constants of the behaviour of energy in space in "compartments."

When he returned to Australia, he conducted the research that showed that while he thought he had the equivalent of twelve chakras or major energy centres, the constants he had derived from his experimental measurements actually coincided with the 96 acupuncture meridians he had found that make up the body-field. And when linked into "compartments," the 96 meridians elegantly reduced themselves to twelve major groups.

Many people have been intrigued with the chakras, with how they correspond with the body and how they work in bio-energetic medicine. Fraser had been intrigued too; he had even gone to Hindu gurus to ascertain as much as possible about these "wheels of energy" and was told that they are in fact spherical field structures going from the back to the front of the body. But now it was clear that the idea of the physics constants went beyond the concept of chakras. Fraser's actual measurements of the traditional chakras confirmed what many had postulated - they form around nerve plexuses, as indeed the entire body-field must. But when energy moves, it creates a field. Stationary energy produces nothing. So instead of looking at major nerve interchanges, Fraser decided we are looking at major structures in the body-field. The result of Fraser's new work on the physics constants was that his entire body-field test, which had taken twenty years to develop, was suddenly obsolete. It needed to be reworked to include the constants as the basis of body-field correction and measurement or assessment.

Once he had completed this work and prepared new "remedies" accordingly, Fraser found the new preparations had rapid and strong effects on the body-field. Fraser and Massey felt they were on the verge of success with making a reliable clinical device. From 2003 to 2004, they worked on developing a new assessment system, and the result is the NES-Professional, a system now in use by hundreds of clinicians. They believe that the NES-Professional is a genuine advance in bio-energetic science and an effective system of health assessment that complements traditional medicine.

Their theory is now easier to understand as well. What organizes the body-field? How is information transfer crucial? How does it work? How does the break down of the body-field contribute to illness? Nutri-Energetics has a comprehensive theory that provides satisfying answers. To explain it in layman's terms, let us use an analogy. Imagine a huge concert hall with structural defects that lead to lousy acoustics. Sound is distorted. Amplification of the sound only makes the distortions worse. This is an analogy of the root of all sickness: the way in which the sound travels causes distortion of information. We have not moved so far from the Hahnemanian idea that disease is caused by "untunement" as he called it in his classic work, *The Organon*. However, NES can explain why and how the "untunement" happens through quantum electrodynamic properties in the body. This is revolutionary because we can do so by bridging biology and physics; and bridging biochemical medicine and energy medicine. *The "untunement" occurs in the way in which subatomic particles are arranged in space, rather than from some variation of their frequency.* Fraser's elegant and comprehensive theory of the human body-field rests upon this foundation.

Quantum Chemistry

NES shows that the body-field is the master control system of the biochemical processes of the body. At the fundamental level (quantum chemistry), chemical reactions are about the making and breaking of chemical bonds. Bonding and hence chemical reactions depend on how electrons order themselves in atoms and molecules. Quantum chemistry defines the rules on how nuclei and electrons spontaneously arrange themselves into structures in space. These structures may be perturbed by fields or given quanta of energy e.g. from photons and electrons that cause them to reorder themselves or in other words, cause a chemical reaction.

The body-field is autocephalic (able to direct itself) because it follows inherent rules that belong to the structures not only of the body, but also according to some of the fundamental rules of quantum physics itself. At the quantum level, molecules can be thought of as structures in space, which when aligned in certain ways are able to interact with other structures and as a result precipitate chemical reactions. The body-field, due to its structure, is responsible for directing the electronic structure of molecules within the body so they not only control information transfer, but influence all chemical reactions as well. Hence, the body-field can be considered the master control system for all metabolism and growth.

This model has previously been partially proposed by other scientists, including Matti Pitkanen and Freeman Cope. Cope produced pivotal work linking physics and biology and developed a solid-state theory of biological processes. He deduced that the activity in the cell is not just electrochemical, and looked at the cell function as if the organelles were three-dimensional semiconductors. He thought that all the structures within the cell could be considered to be in a field in which there is a constant interaction between all subatomic particles, not just between the charges on electrons. His overall view was that superconductive pathways play a controlling role in biological functions. NES work has moved on from here, as we have actually been able to map out the structure of the body-field as well as which parts of it controls which bodily systems.

Chapter 8
Measuring the Quantum Electrodynamic Body-Field

"In fact, biologists are trying to interpret as much as they can about life in terms of chemistry, and, as I have already explained, the theory behind chemistry is quantum electrodynamics."

– Richard Feynman, *QED: The Strange Theory of Light and Matter*

Fraser needed a way to measure his proposed body-field and since no technology existed to do that, he was forced to devise one. The NES–Professional System™ has now replaced that technology; however, we will provide a brief overview of the ideas that led to the development of this revolutionary device.

As has already been briefly discussed, the foundation of the early apparatus was an electrodermal screening device. Fraser first encountered these types of devices about thirty years ago. They work by detecting slight changes in the conductivity of the skin in the presence of light and a weak electromagnetic field. An "effect" is said to occur if there is a movement of more than 15 units (on a scale of 1-100) in the skin conductivity when a structurally imprinted ampoule is put in the circuit.

There has been much speculation over how electrodermal screening devices work. They are poorly understood and often confused with being purely electronic devices. (Conventional scientists reject them altogether.) Fraser came to a different, almost heretical conclusion: if a machine utilizes the electron, then it should work whenever electricity is supplied. There should be no other parameter for its use. However, in a fortuitous experimental mishap, Fraser discovered that no "effects" could be seen when these machines were used in the dark even if they were supplied with electricity. Fraser followed the logic, light = photons; darkness = few or no photons, and determined that the device he was using must somehow be relying upon photon exchange, rather than on the flow of electrons. This led him to coin the term "Photon-Induced Superconductivity" (PIS) in relation to the observed effects of certain of these machines.

The Photon-Induced Superconductivity Effect

The PIS effect is an important part of Fraser's evidence for the body-field. He can measure this effect both with his basic experimental set-up and with the new software technique used in the NES–Professional™. With the early set-up, he showed that he could detect whether a solution A was structurally imprinted or not by measuring changes in skin conductivity when solution A was placed next to an imprinted solution that was known to be A. Fraser calls this a "matching" technique. He had shown that when two identically imprinted solutions are in close proximity in the presence of photons (in the case of the early experimental apparatus used in daylight) and a weak electromagnetic field, a super-conductive effect is induced in the body. This effect could then be measured by the changes in the conductivity of the skin. If the substances were not an identical match, no PIS effect was detected. Therefore, if a single structurally imprinted solution representing a part of the body-field was placed close to the body, a PIS effect would be detected, as two identical entities are "matched."

This matching technique works because of quantum entanglement and can be compared to Cooper Pairs of electrons in superconducting metals or the experiment mentioned earlier involving entangled photon transfer across the Danube. The Nobel Prize-winning BCS theory of superconductors states that in a superconducting metal, pairs of electrons are coupled over distance due to interactions with the crystal lattice that they are travelling through.

Fraser's matching experiments verified that when two identical samples of solutions, structures or anything else are placed together in the presence of photons and a weak electrostatic field, the subatomic particles present in the samples are able to interact and influence the body-field. Following on from this revelation, Fraser has shown that when an effect is observed with a structurally imprinted solution in a circuit with an electrodermal screening device, the interaction between the structurally imprinted solution and the body-field is not purely electronic. Rather, there is a quantum interaction between the imprinted solution and the human body-field. Fraser continued his tests eventually showing that structurally imprinted solutions and the magnetic vectors that can be reproducibly derived from them have nothing to do with frequencies. The imprinting process transfers purely magnetic vector information which "tells" the subatomic particles which way to go in the QED field and hence enables subatomic particles to interact with the body-field in certain ways. You can think of magnetic vectors as subatomic directional arrows or signposts in the body.

The Need for Better Measurements

Fraser's early experimental set-up helped him to make a number of pivotal discoveries about the human body-field, but he still faced a number of problems with the measuring apparatus itself. The PIS effect definitely existed, but as a way of detecting this effect, the electrodermal screening device was less than reliable. The device was extremely sensitive to operator influence and hence, under certain conditions, the results of experiments were not conclusive. In addition, Fraser discovered that the body-field has a structure that is ordered and "folded," and this added a layer of complexity to reading the body-field using his basic experimental set-up. In order to read the body-field *correctly* (to understand where any health problems were occurring), the body-field needs to be read in a specific order, so as to 'unfold' the information. By way of analogy, think of a scrunched up map. You cannot read it properly until it is smoothed out. To read the body-field properly, using the machines then in existence, required the operator to devote a great deal of time and energy to experimentation to do the reading and obtain a reliable analysis. Therefore, a new and more objective way of measuring the body-field and its interactions was required. In recent years, there have been amazing technological advances and it was to these that Fraser turned his attention.

His first advance was to create a new machine in partnership with the Australian biologist Bevin Reid. This machine was able to measure the energy spikes that were connected with structurally imprinted ampoules, in a similar way to chemical nuclear magnetic resonance (NMR) research. The experiments performed with this machine provided further evidence of the quantum nature of the body-field and its components, and that the observed magnetic vectors related to real energy.

The real breakthrough however, came when Fraser met Harry Massey in 2002. Fraser was still looking for a machine that could examine all parts of the body-field. Massey had separately been studying possible computerized ways of understanding how information is transferred in the body. He had also begun a search to find rules that govern both how energy is structured and information are transferred within the human body. Fraser and Massey had both reached similar conclusions after considering other research being carried out in the area.

Fraser and Massey had realized that the information gained from measurements of the conductivity of the skin at acupuncture meridian points could only ever be, at most, a partial measurement of the energy transfer in the body. Fraser understood that these measurements were in fact related to photon activity in the body-field. Because his research had shown him that the body-field was in fact made up of overlapping electromagnetic, ionic and magnetic fields that set up the overall QED field, the measurements of photon activity could be giving information about only 20% of the body-field at best. This was yet another reason why the results of experiments conducted with electrodermal screening devices were frequently inaccurate. Fraser and Massey appreciated that they needed to find another way of investigating the *complete* body-field, a technology that could not only match all of the magnetic vectors and structures contained in subfields in the body-field, but that could also record the vectors that make up the overall body-field. Therefore, it would have to be considerably more complex than Fraser's original basic experimental apparatus.

The Interaction of the Body-Field with Computers

Research has shown that computers programmed with certain software have the ability to pick up information transferred via electrons and photons. More than a decade of research from groups such as the Princeton Engineering Anomalies Research program (PEAR) has shown that human consciousness can interact with, or affect, technological systems. The research of Brenda Dunne and Robert Jahn in particular has verified the hypothesis that random processes can be influenced through human consciousness.

There are currently a number of computational devices on the market that claim to be able to detect health problems in the human body and correct those problems. However, the majority of these devices include a "black box" connecting the human and machine, a box that is used on the pretence that it is somehow picking up "frequencies" emitted from the body electronically. Massey has investigated a number of these devices, but found them all to be lacking in one way or another. The results frequently missed major health problems and were limited in their range of possible explanations. Massey found that these machines tended to display results in an almost "wheel of fortune" way, with the thirty or so most likely ailments, out of an illogical list of 1000s of items, being presented.

Faced with the problems of the current computational devices, but knowing that there was a real interaction that could take place between the body-field and computer, Fraser and Massey joined forces with a computer and mathematics expert. The trio set about examining how information was transferred in biology in order to create their own computational system that could mimic nature and therefore, produce accurate assessment results of the body-field. Their research led them to an understanding of how information can be transferred accurately between two QED fields, one from your body-field and the other set up by a computer. This can only be accomplished if the structures of both fields are described in the same way and if the vectors are presented in the same order it takes to unfold the human body-field.

This understanding was furthered when Massey examined the research of Stephen Wolfram, as discussed in his book *A New Kind of Science*, where he shows how many processes from nature can be mimicked by software by applying iterations of simple rules. It is his belief that all of the complexity and apparent randomness of the universe may be able to be explained by such simple self-replicating rules. NES research confirms this.

During the research process, Fraser and Massey also examined and refined the atomic model in order that information could be transferred at a distance. They also managed to link ideas of spin from quantum physics with the inherent spin found within DNA and linked this to what are in all probability zero-energy pathways of the human body-field. However, most importantly, by putting together all their research they succeeded in creating a new methodology for medical investigation and a device that is able to display the human body-field on a normal computer.

Chapter 9
The NES Model of the Human Body-Field

"Mapping the human body-field involves discerning intricate webs of relationships. It's about realizing that the body does not find only one correct answer but instead prefers to make the best possible choices under the circumstances."

– Peter Fraser and Harry Massey

As the above quote makes clear, the human body-field is not a mechanistic, Newtonian construct. It is a dynamic web of interrelations among all the physiological processes that the body must perform, as well as between these processes and the emotions and consciousness. Moreover, the body-field is in constant interaction with the environment, influenced by and responding to geopathic stress, magnetic fields, toxins, stress, and the like. Fraser has found that the loss of homeostasis - that is, the breakdown of the body's ability for self-correction - is an intricate interplay of almost infinite parameters. What allowed Fraser to uncover the structure of the body-field and to "match" function with information flow was the realization that, despite what geneticists and biochemists might think, the body does not have one "correct" state of being, although there is an optimal preference. While there are some functions of the body that must be maintained within extremely precise parameters, most have flexibility built into them. If they did not, *Homo sapiens* may have gone the way of the dinosaurs. NES has begun to unravel this web of relationships and to understand the "optimal" preferences for the flow of information, but makes no claims that its theory is complete. Fraser and Massey have only begun to crack the code of the human body-field, and they remain humbled by its intricacy and intelligence. Below are the highlights of their research to date, although for the purposes of this book, they provide only a general overview.

Structure of the Human Body Field (HBF)

According to NES research, the human body-field is comprised of many subfields that are in constant interaction and when combined make up the overall body-field. The body-field is both external and internal to the physical body and each is interdependent with the other. That is, the physical body needs the body-field to function correctly, but the body-field arises out of field interactions taking place within the physical body and so is dependent upon it. As Fraser built up a more and more detailed model of the body-field, he found that it has an organized structure. Although he stresses that the sets of *magnetic vectors* that correspond to the different parts of the body-field do not represent frequencies, the different *compartments* of the body-field can be related to energy of different wavelengths. He has found that the body-field is "structured" into 12 "compartments," or quantized levels, each representing a band of energy wavelengths *and* magnetic vectors in the QED field.

These compartments, called Energetic Integrators in NES, are folded, in a similar way to Bohm's folded implicate order, and that is why skill is required in the reading of the body-field. This is one of the major reasons why the earlier methods of investigating the body-field, such as by using electrodermal screening devices, were not always reliable. In a folded system, the structure of the body-field must be comprehensively understood, so that the information can be sequenced in the correct order. If this order is misunderstood, then the results of any assessment of the body-field can be badly skewed. As an aside, any computational device or system also needs to be programmed with a template or "map" of the optimal body-field before it can begin to detect any deviations in the client's field. Fraser and Massey's creation of the NES–Professional™, a software-based system for evaluating the human body-field, contains such a map and represents an innovative and groundbreaking leap forward in bioenergetic assessment. However, there is more to the body-field than the Energetic Integrators. Fraser identifies Energetic Drivers, which power the body-field, and other kinds of energetic features, such as Energetic Terrains, cavities and more. Below is a brief overview of the human body-field (HBF) according to the NES model and important premises relating to it.

NES Follows Quantum Logic

The NES view of the body-field is based on the principles of quantum physics (QED in particular), not biochemistry. An NES scan does not assess the body-field for anything that might be deemed harmful from an allopathic perspective. Instead, it is looking solely for whether subatomic information pathways and interactions that control all physiological processes are damaged, distorted or blocked. If they are, then the NES Infoceuticals provide the corrective QED information to correct the damage, distortions or blocks. Because NES is working with QED information and not biochemistry, the NES Infoceuticals do not interfere with any supplements, homeopathic remedies, herbs, pharmaceuticals, and the like that a person may be taking. In addition, because NES corrects the human body-field (HBF), restoring proper information flow, the effects of other modalities - such as acupuncture, homeopathy and so on - can actually be enhanced.

NES Covers the Entire Energy Range

Unlike other biotechnologies that deal mostly with frequencies, the NES model includes the broader energy range in its understanding of and evaluation of the HBF. We include an assessment of phonic (sub-sonic and extremely low frequency sound), ionic, magnetic and photonic (light) energies.

The Components of the Human Body-Field

The HBF is the body's master control system. A dynamic, layered structure provides a healthy environment for the cellular activity and homeostasis. The body-field is comprised of Big Fields, Energy Drivers, Energetic Integrators, Energetic Terrains, and cavities. We will deal with only some of these aspects of the HBF below.

Big Fields

NES recognizes the impact of Earth fields on the body and the body-field. We identify the Big Field aspect of the HBF as influenced by gravity, the polar magnetic field and the equatorial field. We also recognize Polarity, which is a field concerned with misalignments to various other Earth fields. This is a particular problem for people now since many of us live far from where we were born, continually uproot ourselves by moving to new places and travel constantly by car and airplane. Before any long-term and lasting healing can take place, a person's body-field must be harmoniously aligned with these Earth fields.

Energetic Drivers

Sixteen Energetic Drivers provide the energy needed to maintain the the macro Drivers develop as the embryo develops. Our research indicates that there are three main energy systems that contribute towards the powering energy of the body-field. The Source energy is the first of these macro Drivers. It is energy that is pulled into a living system from the environment and is similar to the fundamental "life" energy that is called, in other cultures, *qi, chi,* or *prana.* It can be thought of as our constitutional energy because it is the catalyst for all life activities. Source energy may be zero-point energy and is dealt with by the body in complex ways that we will not go into here, but it is mostly stored by the many cavities of the body - cranium, thorax, and abdomen and so on. Without Source energy, a person lacks vigour, enthusiasm, hardiness and will.

As the embryo develops, so does the next macro Energetic Driver: the Heart Driver. The heart is one of the first organs to be formed in an embryo, starting to beat after 40 days. The pressure waves induced by the beating of the heart create phonons (subsonic) and extremely low frequency sounds that power the body-field of the embryo. The heart plays other major roles in the NES system of the HBF because it is the most important "imprinter" of information for the body-field, but that is beyond the scope of this book. The basic point here is that the complex sound waves created by the heart, together with the impulses from the nervous system and the energy created from oxygen interchange in the lungs are major contributors to the body-field.

The third Energetic Driver is the Nervous System Driver. The nervous system creates sounds in a similar way to the heart and creates huge amounts of ionized particles. It also contributes to the creation of a polarization wave, which can act as a carrier for the quantum information in the accompanying field.

The last macro Energetic Driver is the Lung Driver. It initiates energetic movement throughout the body and is related to growth, development and more. Most ancient traditions, especially the Yogic traditions, understood how important breathing is to regulating body functions. Using only sound and breathing techniques, a trained Tibetan monk can raise his body temperature enough to dry a wet blanket draped around his shoulders even though he may be sitting outside in frigid conditions.

The micro Drivers are related to other major organ systems of the body and include Skin, Liver, Immunity, Muscles, Stomach, Cell, Kidney, Bone, Thymus and Pancreas.

Without the power provided by the Energetic Drivers, the body cannot function properly. Certainly, healing cannot take place. One of the first signs of illness is often fatigue. Damage to the Drivers comes from a variety of factors - heavy metals and chemical toxins, trauma, emotional shock, electromagnetic pollution, geopathic stress - and reduces the overall strength of the HBF and its effectiveness in regulating life processes. In the NES model of healing, Drivers must be corrected before the Energetic Integrators are dealt with.

Energetic Integrators

There are 12 main Energetic Integrators. They are "compartments" that are similar to meridians in that they cover the information regulation of a range of seemingly unrelated physiological processes. Integrators exist in the DNA field as magnetic vectors that direct subatomic particles along zero-energy pathways. They are structured into information "sections" that deal with different kinds of information in a sequence from nucleic acid to cells, tissues, organs, organ systems, emotions and consciousness. Disease, or what is called self-organizing breakdown, is found near the top of the Integrators.

The Energetic Integrators direct all physiological function. They are like route maps along which QED information is passed in the body, so that cells, DNA and the like receive and send proper instructions for optimal functioning. When Integrators become distorted by toxins, microbes, radiation and so on, the result is inefficient or incorrect cellular and organ communication, disruption of body regulation processes and metabolic exhaustion.

NES views all control mechanisms in the body as information transfer processes. If you step back from the biochemical model, you will see the difference between the two models. In biochemistry, for example, white blood cells recognize and destroy cells and microbes foreign or harmful to the body. There are complex chemical reactions and tagging processes that allow this action to unfold. However, from a bioenergetic perspective, we have to ask, "What is the "information" behind the chemical mechanisms?" If a white blood cell does not have the correct information, the tagging system can go awry and attack the wrong cells or systems, which can result in an autoimmune disorder. It is this kind of information exchange, at the QED level of electrons and photons that determines physiological functioning, including the biochemical processes.

To use an analogy to explain the difference between the biochemical and the bioenergetic, think of a bus ticket. There is the substance of the ticket - the paper that makes it up. Then there is the information that makes the ticket a ticket - it is printed with a value, a bus company name, and other information that gives the piece of paper its identity as a bus ticket. The words on the ticket must be understandable to the people using it for the ticket to be useful. So while you have a physical ticket, its function is determined almost entirely by the information it carries or conveys. There is the real (the paper the ticket is printed on) and the virtual (the information printed on the paper that determines its meaning). Society arises from a foundation of real versus virtual (matter and information) and so does the human body. In NES, the function of the Energetic Integrators is to ensure that the right information gets to the right place at the right time so that the body can use it. This process presupposes an order or sequence and NES is the only model that has unravelled this optimal sequence and uses it as part of the protocol practitioners follow when working with clients.

More Details about the Energetic Integrators

As we have said, the human body-field is comprised of 12 energy compartments (or structures), which provide the zero-energy pathways for information transfer to the relevant cells in the body. In fact, it is DNA itself, which is also split into 12 main sections, that supplies the framework for the transfer of information in the body. There are also links between the ways Integrators work and how the 12 main acupuncture meridians are able to communicate information throughout the body and how the cells in the relevant area are able to pick up information from the framework of DNA in the cells.

Each Energetic Integrator represents the structure of a part of DNA. The magnetic vectors of the Integrators are situated around DNA and provide direction to QED information in the body. Within the Energetic Integrators, and indeed within all of the NES Infoceuticals, information is carried on a quantized wave. The structure and hence the nature of this quantized wave is determined by the DNA. However, they do not actually occupy the same space as every spin of a real particle is accompanied by a double spin in quantum. Therefore, for every 360 degree-spin of DNA, we get a 720-degree spin of the quantized structure. The idea of structure conveying information is observed in nature. For one example, next time you are near any stalactites, have a closer look at them. You will see that every stalactite, no matter how young or old, big or small, has followed the same energy compartment-type of growth pattern and has a 720 degree twist from top to bottom. The body manages information by storing it within spatial "memory." Imagine this space a bit like a corkscrew, and the rule is that any part of the corkscrew is able to communicate with any other part of the corkscrew *that shares the same angle*, in other words if they have the same spin.

What do the Energetic Integrators and structure of DNA have to do with disease? Most of us are familiar with the shape of the DNA double helix and we understand that it is a continually rotating strand of nucleic acids. Every Energetic Integrator is able to rotate by 720 degrees. Different types of quantized information are carried at various degrees of spin within the Integrators, starting from nutritional mineral information and ending at pathology. Our research shows that all pathology (i.e. illness) is found above a 660-degree spin and this is where the quantized wave begins to break up before starting afresh at the next Integrator (0-degree spin). In practice, this means that if the structure of the quantized information below a 660-degree spin has been distorted, for example by genetic damage or through environmental factors, it leads to a breakdown in the wave function above 660 degrees. When the wave begins to break up, there are major distortions of information, leading to pathology or disease. Due to patent considerations, we cannot discuss all of the relevant information regarding the Energetic Integrators; however, we can tell you that the more serious diseases tend to occur in the upper Integrators EI 9 through 12.

Energetic Terrains

Energetic Terrains are part of advanced protocols in the NES system, so we will only touch on them here. Fraser has found that the real and virtual must be taken into account when explaining how viruses and bacteria and other microbes compromise the body. Quantum biology suggests that magnetic fluctuations of the Earth can power a process that spins out information structures in space, or "pictures," from cellular

DNA. These "virtual" structures can be seen as energetic templates, which NES calls Energetic Terrains (ETs). The ETs provide an environment that is supportive to real microbes, which can thrive there and generate both acute and chronic illnesses.

A further requirement for the formation of Energetic Terrains is that the DNA must contain errors. These errors may result from real microbes interfering with cellular DNA or from blockages caused by misalignment of the body with the Earth's Big Fields. This is one reason for the priority of aligning Big Fields beginning with the first NES visit.

Our research shows thus, that DNA errors in the cells of certain tissues in a distorted magnetic field combine to produce Energetic Terrains. They usually form slowly, although they may occur instantly from a large shock that is imprinted on the body-field or over several days when there is a severe magnetic storm. The effect of the sort of field errors we call Energetic Terrains is to provide a host environment for virtual microbes, where they can hide, shield real microbes, and weaken the immune system so that these microbes cannot be detected within the local tissue. Thus, infectious microbes can remain in tissue undetected, even though they are active.

Another feature of Energetic Terrains is that they can become masked (hidden). That is, when one Terrain is corrected, another may appear, as if from nowhere, because the previous error was masking the presence of the other Terrain. Fraser and Massey suspect that major chronic diseases, such as HIV, AIDS, cancer, Chronic Fatigue Syndrome, diabetes and others are associated with multiple Energetic Terrains. We have found that Terrains tend to overlap in a particular order and so they must be corrected in a specific sequence. In the NES protocol plan, Energetic Terrains usually are not dealt with until at least the fourth clinical visit.

Examples of Energetic Terrains include:

ET Type 0 Central Nervous System, dealing with microbes associated with live-virus vaccines such as for polio.

ET Type 5 Skin and Lungs, dealing with a broad spectrum of viruses, including Human Papilloma virus, Bunya virus family and Herpes.

ET Type 9 Stomach and Duodenum, dealing with bacteria, Helicobacter Pylori, Escherichia coli (E-coli) and the Salmonella family.

The Map of the Body-Field

The above information provides a glimpse into the structure of the human body-field that Fraser uncovered over nearly 25 years of research. His complete understanding of the body-field includes an immense amount of precise information about how Energetic Drivers, Integrators, Terrains and other aspects of the body-field relate to specific physiological functions. By putting all of this information together, Fraser was able to create the world's first detailed "map" of the human body-field, which integrates the energetic functions of the body with its biochemical functions. In collaboration with Harry Massey, Fraser was able to encode that map into computer software to make an easy-to-use clinical device to assess the body-field. This device is called the NES–Professional™. When you place your hand on the input device, the software is able to "read" your body-field, through a process of quantum entanglement of like structures, compare it against the "optimal" map encoded in the software, and note any deviations. The deviations reveal where your body-field is distorted. The software also reveals the NES Infoceuticals that can restore the information necessary to correct your body-field.

A question frequently asked of Fraser and Massey is, "How can there be an optimal map as we're all different?" In fact we are all individuals with different biochemistries and slightly different body-fields, but the main *structure* of our body-fields, especially of the 12 Energetic Integrators and of the information contained within them, is identical to everyone else's. It is this *structure* that makes up the map and that is the propriety work of NES UK, Ltd. In the world of QED, information can be said to be "structured space." It is the *structured space* of the body-field that directs information via subatomic particles to their correct functions in the body. If this structure becomes degraded and hence cellular instructions become distorted, then ill health may result. The understanding of the structure of the HBF is what makes the NES system so different from other systems and so effective as an assessment tool.

The NES Infoceuticals

The NES Infoceuticals are made of micro-minerals suspended in water that act as carriers for specially imprinted QED magnetic vector information. They are taken as drops in water. The information they contain directs the restructuring of the HBF back to as close to an optimal configuration as possible for each individual. Details are explained in the next chapter.

Chapter 10
Introduction to the NES–Professional™

The NES–Professional™ combines Peter Fraser's discovery and mapping of the quantum electro-dynamic human body-field with the simplicity of computer technology to produce the most advanced system for body-field analysis and treatment available. It empowers the therapist, not only to get to the root energetic causes of why a patient may be ill, but also to restore optimal physiological function using the Nutri-Energetics Infoceuticals.

Review of the NES Model of the Body-Field

Your body has energy continuously moving through it, which produces a quantum electro-dynamic field. This body-field can be viewed at many levels:

- In biochemical terms, it can be seen as the supra-chemical control system of the body, which acts as the master control system for all metabolism and growth.

- At the energetic level, it can be viewed as the body's internal and external field (aura) and as the field that homeopathic remedies, acupuncture needles and hands-on healers are able to effect.

- From a quantum electrodynamics perspective, it can be viewed as the magnetic vectors that direct subatomic particles to their optimal positions within the body.

As stated previously, the human body-field (HBF) has structure and consists of magnetic vectors (or signposts), which are able to direct subatomic particles within your body. This is how the HBF can act as the body's master control system above and beyond that of the traditional biochemical system. The QED field information is then carried via subatomic particles to the computer, where NES–Professional™ compares the client's body-field with the map of the optimal human body-field that is coded within the software. It then displays any differences it finds between the optimal map of the human body-field and the client's body-field, and displays the results via a graphical user interface.

The NES Infoceuticals provide the core directions to a client's body-field so that any deviations away from the optimal HBF can be brought back to normal. In other words, the Infoceuticals help the body-field return to its optimal structure so that in its autocephalic capacity (its inherent structure gives it the ability to direct itself) it is able to direct the body once again in the most optimal way for healthy living.

What Kinds of Information Does the NES–Professional™ Display?

NES–Professional™ is the only device to our knowledge that is able to view (graphical interpretation) the entire human body-field. It displays four main types of information:

A) Structural damage done to the QED body-field

- Summary of all aspects of the HBF

- Big Field influences—Gravity, Ionic and Earth's Magnetic fields

- Relative strength of the Energetic Drivers

- Structural status of the Energetic Integrators

B) Current imbalances "symptoms", which are a reflection of damage done to the body-field and which can be corrected using Nutri-Energetics Infoceuticals

- Major organ function assessment

- Musculoskeletal - pinpoints where pain is occurring in the body and recommends Infoceuticals to address any problems

- Food intolerances/Allergies - concentrates not on the intolerances but on the root causes behind them

- Metabolism - base rate, pH balance, carbohydrate, protein, glucose, blood sugar, enzyme creation and function

- Nutrition - concentrates on the root causes behind malabsorption and poor metabolism of vitamins, minerals and fats

- Factors affecting oxygenation

- Current emotional state

- Mental function

- Meridian function

C) Shocks that have caused damage to the body-field

- Environmental influences - what damage has been done to the body-field and what pollutants or factors are problem areas

- Pleomorphic organisms and viruses - information as to why the body's immune system has not been able to react appropriately

- Emotional shocks

- Nutritional deficiencies

D) Complete Treatment Information

- "Help" files containing information about each and every issue displayed by NES–Professional™

- Recommendations for appropriate Infoceuticals for each and every screen

- A Main Report - summarizes the exact readings, to two decimal places, for an at-a-glance overview of all items on the assessment

More About How the NES–Professional™ Works

NES–Professional™ compares the structure of subatomic particles (such as photons and electrons) from your QED body-field with the magnetic vectors encoded in the map of the optimal human body-field. But how can it do this? As we said earlier, Fraser and Massey have worked out the structure of the HBF. In the realm of QED, structured space equates with information flow. There are other factors involved, which are discussed below.

Quantum Entanglement

There is a curious property in physics called quantum entanglement that allows identical arrangements of subatomic particles to communicate with each other, but only if their structures are the same.

Quantum entanglement is a property that allows two particles to behave as one no matter how far apart they are. Measuring the state of one particle instantaneously determines the state of the other. An example is Cooper Pairs of electrons in super-conducting metals. The Nobel Prize-winning BCS theory of super-conductors states that in a super-conducting metal, pairs of electrons are coupled over distance, due to interactions with the crystal lattice that they are travelling through. In other words, they share the same structure and can therefore communicate to each other over distance. Research into quantum entanglement and other associated quantum effects have lent experimental validity to the theory of the inherent quantum interconnectedness in the universe.

So, the main challenge when Fraser and Massey created the NES–Professional™ was to produce within the system something that mimicked what occurred in nature, or in other words to make sure the structure mapped into the computer was identical to the HBF so that information could be transferred efficiently between two QED fields.

Interaction of QED Fields

One needs energy for a QED field to be set up and for the body-field to interact with. It probably does not take much imagination to realize that a computer - through its constant on/off switching - is continuously producing a QED field. This is the field that sets up and initiates the interaction with the client's QED field and that begins the assessment process. Because of this method of performing the assessment scan, the NES–Professional™ is much more independent of the operator's/practitioner's influence than are almost all other biotechnologies currently available that claim to scan the body's energy field.

The Nutri-Energetics Infoceuticals

As described briefly in the previous chapter, the NES Infoceuticals are imprinted with QED information that restores the body-field and hence the body, to proper functioning. They contain corrective information, so that regulation processes in the body return to homeostasis. The Infoceuticals cannot be used alone. Their use is tied to the scan results and to the proper unfolding of the body-field in the proper sequence. In the NES protocol of unfolding the body-field, the Big Fields must be balanced first, followed by the Drivers, Integrators and Terrains in that order. Therefore, NES does not sell Infoceuticals to the general public. The following information provides more explanation about how the Infoceuticals work.

The NES Infoceuticals Contain QED Information

Nutri-Energetics has devised a method of imprinting subatomic particles, as magnetic vector information, into a base of organic colloidal minerals. When a person takes the drops, the sub-atomic particles then act as magnetic signposts in a client's body-field. From Fraser's perspective, this subatomic "signpost" process is the best explanation for how homeopathy actually works.

For a greater understanding of how only a few drops of liquid can have such a dramatic effect, we go back to our discussion of quantum physics and how similar structures are able not only to communicate with each other but also to change states simultaneously. Each Infoceutical's structure is similar to both the geno-field and to certain organelles, which ensures rapid uptake of the messages imprinted in an Infoceutical. This information is picked up by the organelles of the cells, in various parts of the body, whose role is controlling the conventional biochemical systems to do their job of eliminating toxins and bringing the body back to proper functioning.

Zero-Energy Pathways and Information Flow

Information always is transferred from one part of the HBF to another part of it and the pathway taken, in accordance with the laws of physics, must be that which takes the least amount of energy to transfer that data. This pathway can be called the zero-energy pathway and it is crucial to keeping normal physiology going. According to NES theory, what happens when you get sick? At first, the body is able to keep the appearance of health by simply forcing the information transfer to take another route, although it will be a less efficient one. By taking this alternate, less ideal pathway, information can become distorted, degraded, and even misdirected. Forcing information along a less efficient route also takes energy, which is why the first signs of illness are often fatigue or general malaise, which often grows worse as the information transfer process continues to break down over time.

The NES Infoceuticals however, have been designed to correct these pathways and processes. The Drivers provide much-needed energy/power to the body. The Integrators correct pathway structures and regulation processes. As one uses the Infoceuticals, fatigue may continue for a while as the body works to correct the breakdown in information flow. However, once the information transfer problems have been resolved and pathways are restored or corrected, the body needs less energy and so vigour is returned. In reality, the process is more complicated, since as the body is restored to proper functioning, it will begin to deal with problems that have been masked, such as toxin load. However, in the simplest terms, the Infoceuticals work because more information flowing along the correct pathways equates with enhanced health.

Chapter 11
NES and Other Healing Modalities

NES and Homeopathy

NES, because it is based on QED field science and quantum biology, is able to explain more clearly how other healing modalities work. For example, it provides a clearer explanation for homeopathy and gives us a place to be able to both prove it and improve it dramatically.

Homeopathic remedies, whether made through succussions or electronically, work in a way similar theoretically to how NES Infoceuticals work; that is, subatomic particles become imprinted with information that can provide directions to the body-field about how to better execute a particular action. Traditional homeopaths were experts at finding the analogues of plants and minerals, but what they lacked was an understanding of how these analogues must resemble the body-field in some way or another. NES advances homeopathy in that we can use direct sets of data that represent the body-field more accurately.

Homeopathy works through using a diluted substance that is meant to provide the body the symptoms of a particular disease. A relatively healthy body-field is then able to react against this message and, it is hoped, provide the correct message to rid the body of those symptoms. However, if the body is too compromised and does not have adequate power, it cannot move the message or effect the change. In addition, in many cases, the homeopathic remedy chosen is one choice from among many, many possibilities and so might not be the right one. At best, it might be a close approximation of what the body needs.

Nutri-Energetics, in contrast, selects the correct message in the first place because our assessment scan can properly "read" the body-field structure and unfold it in the correct sequence. The Infoceutical selected is the one that contains the proper *corrective* message and delivers it *directly* to the body-field, so the body does not have to react against a symptomatic signal. In this way and in several others, the resolution of the problem happens much more quickly with NES and it requires less effort (energy) from the body.

NES preparations are multi-dimensional in that they construct a much more complex image in space of the dynamic function of the body than just a simple dataset. NES Infoceuticals have hundreds of sets of mathematical data within them, each of which must be imprinted in a certain sequence in order to create a correct dynamic effect. The method of imprinting this data in sequence without destroying the integrity of the data is NES proprietary information.

For homeopaths, data degradation is an old problem. After a certain number of dilutions, the remedies cannot be mixed further without causing unwanted data changes. Most homeopaths appear to agree that six mixes is enough. While NES does not use succussion or dilution in making the Infoceuticals, we have had to pay close attention to issues of data integrity. The body-field is extremely complex and to correct it properly a huge amount of data is needed; if the data is corrupted, then the wrong message is given to the body and the results will be negligible or non-existent. NES has, after decades of research and trail and error, been able largely to solve this problem through doing a direct imprint onto a mineral substrate.

NES and Meridians

While Fraser borrowed the homeopathic idea of working with energetic analogues for his research, he also incorporated ideas from Traditional Chinese Medicine. In his early research, Fraser catalogued the energetic equivalents of 96 energy channels in the body that exactly followed the *jing–luo*, or the acupuncture meridians used in a system developed by the Chinese more than 1500 years. (Fraser wrote a degree-level acupuncture course that is still in use at the university-level in Australia.) Most Westerners are familiar with 12 major meridians; others know about additional meridians, including the group of connecting meridians. Nevertheless, the entire system, which is described in classical Chinese texts, consists of many more meridians than these: there are at least 90 meridians, not counting the many small meridians that branch from the main ones. The system is complex and takes many years to learn well.

Fraser found that one group of meridians, called the Divergent Meridians, communicates with material found in DNA and RNA samples, a development that is of prime importance in the theory of bioenergetics as developed by the NES. Other groups of meridians were found by Fraser to correspond energetically to different types of connective tissues, of which there are many in the body. During his research on the body-field, Fraser always found specific connections between the groups of four Divergent Meridian energetic analogues he had made. When he sought a reason, he was always drawn back to field theory. In particular, he thought of English biologist Rupert Sheldrake's theory of morphogenetic fields. Fraser surmised that DNA and RNA generate a morphogenetic field when placed in a QED field - but only then.

Put another way, he theorized that there are four stranded nucleic acids that are energetically the same as his four Divergent Meridian analogues. What he found was the distinction between "is" and "like," which is a big difference in science. In fact, it turns out that the energetic analogues of groups of four Divergent Meridians look very much like groups of four nucleic acids called G-quadruplex DNA. Research on G-quadruplex DNA which has four-stranded conformation, by Dr Shankar Balasubramian at Cambridge University is ongoing. Quoting from his website: "G-quadruplexes are four-stranded DNA conformations that can be adopted by DNA sequences from a number of regions of the human genome. The formation of such structures can influence biological processes that include cell divisions and the expression of certain genes."

Even though we can provide only a glimpse of the theoretical foundation upon which NES is built, we hope we have made it clear that NES is the culmination of many lines of inquiry and research: Traditional Chinese Medicine, acupuncture, homeopathy, biochemistry and quantum electrodynamics to name just a few. Although research continues and we are continually refining our processes, we are confident that because of our understanding of the map of the optimal HBF, how to unfold it in sequence, and how to imprint information without loss of data integrity, NES results are more accurate and consistent than any other biotechnology currently available.

The remainder of this book provides an overview of specific aspects of the NES assessment software and the Infoceuticals.

Section C

NES and the
NES–Professional™

Chapter 12:
NES Infoceuticals and Assessment Overview

Below is general information about the Big Field, Energetic Driver, and Energetic Integrator Infoceuticals and the relevant assessment screens on the NES–Professional™ software.

The Big Fields

This screen reports on the body's alignment with Earth's three "big fields." These are significant energy fields produced by the Earth that correspond with gravity, the magnetic poles and the equator, 90 degrees to the magnetic poles. Body misalignment with these fields can cause health issues and restrict the body's ability to adapt and change to a healthier state of being. This screen also reports on the integrity of the body's electromagnetic polarity. Both the big fields and polarity are priority areas addressed in all NES clinical visits.

- The body is naturally adapted to a slow pace, with rest periods to maintain alignment and natural harmony with the Earth.

- Constant movement at high speed (car, train and airplane), artificial sound, chemical toxins, and light and magnetic influences can all cause Big Field alignment issues.

The Vertical Axis

The vertical axis is generated by gravity.

- Misalignment can be associated with long-term effects of geopathic stress (subterranean waterways, mineral deposits or caves).

- Misalignment can be associated with slight variations in gravity from place to place.

- Linked with functional problems of the nervous system and can affect sleep patterns.

- Linked to noticeable health variances depending on whether person is upright or lying down.

The Magnetic Polar Axis

The magnetic polar axis is generated by the magnetic poles of the Earth.

- Misalignment is associated with the body's processes of creating and distributing heat. May result in hot and cold regions randomly located about the body.

The Equatorial Axis

This axis is placed at 90 degrees to the Earth's north-south magnetic polar axis.

- Misalignment of this axis may reduce the body's ability to absorb the right trace minerals from food.

- Metabolic diseases can be associated with misalignment of this axis. Oxidation and anti-oxidation process may be affected.

- The liver and the large bowel processes may also be affected.

Big Field Infoceutical Protocol

The general clinical rule is: If on a scan any of the three big field axes have an indicator that is not zero or the Big Field

Aligner is indicated, the client needs the Big Field Aligner (BFA) Infoceutical. If polarity is not zero, the client should take the Polarity Infoceutical to normalize electromagnetic polarity. The Polarity Infoceutical contains BFA as part of its formulation and thus if polarity and any big fields are distorted, only the Polarity Infoceutical is required.

Big Field Aligner Infoceutical

The Big Field Aligner (BFA) Infoceutical has the capacity to correct field misalignments between the Earth's three big fields (vertical, polar and equatorial) and the human body-field.

- The bar graph gives a summary indicating the need for the Big Field Aligner.

- Correcting these axes misalignments is crucial for opening the pathway for healing.

- If the BFA reading is zero but one or more of the three field axes are not zero, then BFA should be used.

Polarity Infoceutical

The sum of the body's biological and atomic activities generates an overall electromagnetic field that fully encapsulates the body. This field plays a vital role in the formation of the human body-field and its quantum level activity. If this field becomes negatively charged and/or adopts a left-hand spin, there will be huge disruption to the quantum fields.

- It is quite difficult for the body to engender positive change unless polarity is normalized.

- Emotional blocks, stress, electromagnetic disturbances of all kinds, air travel, geopathic stress, toxins and chronic illness can all create polarity issues.

- The Polarity Infoceutical is used to re-establish polarity to its original, optimal state.

- The Polarity Infoceutical also corrects for Big Field misalignments and therefore should *not* be taken in conjunction with the BFA Infoceutical.

The Energetic Drivers

This screen reports on the integrity of the body's 16 Energetic Drivers (EDs). According to bioenergetic theory, the human body-field (HBF) is responsible for overall coordination of physical, chemical, neural and energetic activity within the body. For the HBF to do this work correctly it needs to be energized and this is the job of 16 Energetic Drivers.

- Activity of a chemical, electrical, ionic, sonic, neural and physical nature within physical tissue generates a field energy known as "Driver energy."

- The sum of the Driver energies produced by a specific set of organ tissues forms the Energetic Drivers.

- For example, the heart has many types of activity—sound (lub dub), muscular (cardiac contraction), electrical (pacemaker), etc. The sum of activity within the heart tissues generates a field known as the Heart Driver. The Heart Driver field helps energize the HBF.

- Physical and energetic issue including stress, toxins and emotional shock within the Driver tissue will degrade the integrity of the Driver field and thus upset the HBF balance.

- Each Energetic Driver is associated with the formation (maturation) of specific body cells, particularly the immune cells; thus the Energetic Drivers form an important part in maintaining immune system function.

- NES Energetic Driver (ED) Infoceuticals are designed to restore integrity to Driver fields with the effect of promoting the associated tissue's and the immune system's functional health and energizing the HBF.

Energetic Driver Infoceuticals

Energetic Driver Infoceutical Protocol

- Because of the fundamental need to energize the HBF, Drivers are given priority in the first two NES protocols. They are also commonly used in subsequent protocols.

- ED Infoceuticals (and other Infoceuticals) are numbered according to the sequence of the body-field. The Drivers should be taken in order from lowest number to highest within any given protocol.

- Normally, the recommendation is that no more than four ED Infoceuticals would be prescribed in one protocol period.

- Liver Driver and Pancreas Drivers are not used in the first visit because of their potentially significant detoxification effects.

ED 1 - Source Driver

Source refers to the source of the body's dynamic energy and it probably does not have a chemical equivalent; it is purely a bio-energetic concept, similar to the substance called Yuan Qi (Ocean energy) in Traditional Chinese Medicine that is said to feed the meridian systems of the body.

- Source energy is the catalyst for all chemical and energetic activities in the body. Without it, nothing can happen.

- Source energy is particularly depleted by chronic illness, physical/mental exhaustion, poor breathing, toxic exposure, stress and malnutrition.

- Bacteria, viruses and fungus may also deplete Source energy.

- The Source Driver Infoceutical (ED1) is sometimes referred to as the "Master Energy Driver" or the "Driver of the Drivers" since it directly energizes all the other Drivers.

- The ED 1 Infoceutical should be given priority in any protocol.

- The ED 1 Infoceutical is designed to replenish the Source Energy and thus provide the impetus for healing and correct body function.

- The ED 1 Infoceutical may prove useful in relieving fatigue from detoxification or healing reactions.

- The Source Driver field is associated with the reticulo-endothelial cells involved with ingestion of red blood cells, bacteria and foreign colloidal partials.

ED 2 – Imprinter Driver

Internal body information transfer is crucial to correct regulation and maintenance of body activities. The Imprinter Driver forms a vital part of the information transfer process. The Imprinter Driver field is generated by the heart, which imprints nervous system information into the blood. It also has energetic links with the rough and smooth Endoplasmic Reticulum (ER) and ribosomes found within cells.

- The ED 2 Infoceutical is designed to restore integrity to the Imprinter Driver field and thus ensures optimal information transfer within in the body.

- The ED 2 Infoceutical is classed as a "feel good" preparation and tends to engender positive emotions; it emotionally uplifts and facilitates charisma.

- The ED2 Infoceutical is often used early in a protocol due to its effect in correcting metabolism through its action on cellular Endoplasmic Reticulum, whose functions include protein and lipid synthesis, detoxification, inter- and intra-cellular molecular transportation, conversion of cholesterol to steroids, and detoxifying foreign proteins.

ED 3 – Cell Driver

Cellular energy and the Cell Driver fields are generated by tiny structures called mitochondria that are present in all cells. Cells require energy to perform their daily activities; without it, they cannot function and will die. The liver has the most intense cellular activity, so this Driver is particularly linked with it and general metabolism. Toxins and other environmental factors can disrupt the ability of cells to generate the required energy and function correctly.

- The ED 3 Infoceutical is designed to help the mitochondria generate energy and facilitate normal cellular respiration and excretion. It does this partly through aiding the excretion of Dioxins, PCPs, Xylenes and the effects of electromagnetic radiation.

- The Cell Driver energetically communicates with mast cells, which are involved with forming anticoagulants in blood to inhibit clotting in the vessels, as well as antibody immunoglobulin E (associated with allergic reactions).

- The ED 3 Infoceutical has been indicated as an aid to ease the effects of geopathic stress.

- The ED 3 Infoceutical may have the effect of aiding body metabolism generally, particularly that of the Liver and waste product excretion.

- The ED 3 Infoceutical combines well with various anti-oxidants, which are responsible for mopping up free radicals, in addition to having a strong anti-oxidant effect itself.

ED 4 – Nervous System Driver

The nervous system helps control and integrate all body activities by sensing changes, interpreting them and reacting. It uses complex electrochemical signals and patterns, which include brain waves, to achieve this and generates the Nervous System Driver field. The Western lifestyle of over-stimulation, sensory overload and mental over-activity can disturb the brain waves, particularly the delta waves (deep sleep) and alpha waves (relaxation).

- The ED 4 Infoceutical is designed to correct the balance of delta and alpha waves to promote a feeling of calmness and aid restful sleep.

- The ED 4 Infoceutical promotes the generation of the nervous system energetic field as a whole, which is required for correct nervous system function and restoring of neurological integrity.

- The Nervous System Driver field helps with the maturation process of the neuroblasts (embryonic nerve cells).

- Nervous system energy fields are adversely affected by the following pollutants, which the ED 4 Infoceutical has been designed to help remove at the energetic level:

  ○ Butanols (hydrocarbon solvents)

- Chlorpyrifos (common organophosphate pesticide)
- Heptane (solvent)
- Diphtheria vaccination
- Rabies vaccination
- Tetanus vaccination

ED 5 – Circulation Driver

The circulation of the blood is the biggest physical movement within the body, with some 7000 litres per day (1540 gallons) circulating. This movement generates a Driver field known as Circulation. The state of the Circulation Driver field is reflective of many factors having to do with blood and its flow.

- The ED 5 Infoceutical has been designed to restore integrity to the Circulation Driver field.

- This field is an indicator of how well the arterial circulation system transfers blood and thus ultimately its ability to transfer oxygen, waste products and information.

- The Circulation Driver field provides a guide to the state of the erythrocytes (red blood cells) and efficacy of oxygen hemoglobin.

- A person's emotional state affects blood circulation and thus the field it generates.

- The Circulation Driver will also register the state of the nerve plexuses that affect circulation.

ED 6 – Heart Driver

The heart and its Driver field are associated with the heart's physical, muscular pumping action and the creation of complex double sound waves. There is also a strong emotional content to the heart field. Activity within the heart tissue generates the Heart Driver field.

- The ED 6 Infoceutical has been designed to re-establish integrity to the Heart Driver field.

- The Heart Driver field is associated with decision-making processes, identity, clarity, self-confidence and mental integration. When it is damaged, self-esteem can drop to low levels.

- Damage to the Heart Driver field may affect the sounds of the heart, the pulse, and the ability to transfer information around the body.

- The most likely causes of errors in the Heart Driver field are shock, stress and pollutants.

- The Heart Driver field is also affected by the following pollutants, which the ED 6 Infoceutical has been designed to remove at an energetic level:

    - 4-phenylcyclohexene (carpet backing)

    - Dioxane (industrial solvent)

    - Measles-Mumps-Rubella vaccination

- The Heart Driver field assists with the maturation process of the immune system's platelets, lymphocytes and monocytes.

- The Heart Driver field is linked with the mid brain and visual and auditory acuity.

- The ED 6 Infoceutical may be beneficial for hearing acuity and major learning difficulties resulting from autism (particularly linguistic ones).

ED 7 – Lung Driver

The lungs oxygenate blood, excrete CO_2 and water, initiate energetic movement through every tissue of the body and produce sound via the larynx. According to bioenergetics, the combination of these effects produces the Lung Driver field, which activates numerous other energy fields. Airborne toxins (industrial, chemical, agricultural) will tend to accumulate in the lungs and cause damage both physiological and energetic.

- The ED 7 Infoceutical has been designed to reactivate the correct exchange of gases in the bronchioles that fuel the major mechanism of metabolism.

- Increased oxygen in the lungs (to normal levels) aids the reduction of viral infection.

- The Lung Driver field is related to growth, development and the ability to breathe correctly.

- The Lung Driver field can be connected to the higher mental skills in children and higher consciousness levels in adults.

- The Lung Driver field is associated with the maturation process of the erythroblasts, a cell in the red marrow that synthesizes hemoglobin.

- The Lung Driver field does not function well with the following pollutants, which ED 7 has been designed to remove at the energetic level:

  - Butanols, (hydrocarbon solvent)
  - Asbestos

- Vaccinations for Influenza (S, A) Polio, BCG (TB), and Yellow Fever

ED 8 – Stomach Driver

The stomach's primary physiological process is to receive and temporarily store food and drink. Its acidic environment kills off microbes and initiates protein digestion. Energetically, the stomach and large intestine are linked. A mixture of peristaltic movements and chemical reactions involved in the break down and absorption of minerals, proteins, fats and carbohydrates within the GI tract generates the Stomach Driver field. Toxins in the GI tract are detrimental to the Stomach Driver field.

- The ED 8 Infoceutical has been designed to restore integrity to the Stomach Driver field.

- This Driver field reflects the efficiency of the entire digestive process including absorption and assimilation. It is also related to immune system reactions.

- Research indicates this field is also linked to muscle stamina, chronic chest conditions and breathing issues.

- The Stomach Driver assists with the maturation process of granulocytes (granular white blood cells) and basophils.

- The cocktail of "alien" chemicals in today's food means many people's digestive tracts are embedded with a large number of foreign chemicals. This has detrimental effects on the physiological and energetic functions of the stomach.

- Stomach energy fields do not function well with the following pollutants, which ED 8 has been designed to help remove at the energetic level:

  - Fungicides

119

- Electromagnetic radiation

- Heavy metals - Antimony, Cadmium, Lead and Arsenic

- Hepatitis A and B vaccinations

- A short period of strong detox reactions may be experienced with this Driver so it usually started with a minimal number of drops.

ED 9 – Muscle Driver

The muscle system represents the largest group of tissues in the body about half the body weight. The Muscle Driver field is generated as the muscles extend and contract in every day physical actions. Errors can occur in this field when muscles are functioning incorrectly, there is a build up of toxins, or movements become restricted. Past emotions and shocks are also stored within muscles and can affect the field.

- The ED 9 Infoceutical is designed to correct the muscle field by removing any blockages caused by incorrect oxygen uptake, lead pollution or residues of common organisms.

- The ED 9 Infoceutical may also boost the availability of common minerals, such as calcium and magnesium, to the muscle field.

- The ED 9 Infoceutical may be able to improve muscle performance in cases where detoxification is required.

- The muscles and Muscle Driver field can store emotional issues and memories of physical trauma that may form foci of chronic health conditions. The ED 9 Infoceutical is designed to aid muscle field repair and liberate stored emotions and traumas.

- This is a dynamic Infoceutical that centres on the muscle functions and can be used as a key part of neuromuscular therapy of any type.

- The Muscle Driver field is associated with the maturation process of monocyte white blood cells.

- Muscles and joints may actually ache more when chronic arthritis sufferers take the correction to the muscle field.

ED 10 – Skin Driver

The skin is the largest organ in the body and interacts with the vertical axis of the Big Field. Therefore, it is important that it is working optimally. Its major tasks involve respiration and excretion of unwanted products from the body and regulation of fluid and mineral balance. It is also an important defence barrier. The movement of molecules through the surface of the skin via respiration and excretion generates the Skin Driver field.

- The ED 10 Infoceutical has been designed to energize the Skin Driver Field and thus promote the skin's physiological functions.

- The ED 10 Infoceutical may help with skin conditions and muscular problems.

- The ED 10 Infoceutical is designed to aid the removal of metabolic toxins from the body through the skin.

- There are strong links between the Skin and Lung energy fields, so the ED 10 Infoceutical may help with respiratory problems.

- There is also an energetic link with the mucous membranes of the bowels and lungs.

- The Skin Driver field is associated with the maturation process of megakaryocytes (very large bone marrow cells that release mature blood platelets involved in blood coagulation).

ED 11 – Liver Driver

The liver is the chemical factory of the body and performs a multitude of vital processes. The Liver Driver field is generated by the actions of the liver cells.

- The ED 11 Infoceutical has been designed to correct the Liver Driver field and thus aid the liver's physiological processes.

- The liver's functions include metabolizing nutrients, manufacturing hormones and enzymes, generating heat, detoxifying metabolic and ingested toxins, producing bile, storing fats and carbohydrates, filtering the immune system as well as many other functions including blood sugar regulation, blood clotting, pH regulation, etc.

- The Liver Driver field is disturbed by ingested and airborne pollutants, heavy metals, food-based toxins, infective agents as well as stress and poor sleep.

- The Liver Driver field is associated with reticulocytes (regeneration of lost blood) and prothrombin (precursor to a blood clotting agent).

- The ED 11 Infoceutical is not used in the first NES protocol because of its potentially significant detoxification effects.

ED 12 – Kidney Driver

The kidneys form a vital part of the fluid maintenance and blood pressure mechanisms of the body; however, in the broader sense the kidneys include the adrenal glands. Traditional

Chinese Medical identifies the kidneys as the place for storing bio-energy known as *jing*. In addition, according to Traditional Chinese Medicine, the kidney energy affects brain cell function and stamina. The Kidney Driver field is generated by the kidney's functions and the presence of *jing*.

- The ED 12 Infoceutical has been designed to restore the Kidney Driver field where it has become depleted and thus aid its physiological functions.

- The kidney's functions include the filtration of waste from the blood, urine production, reabsorption of electrolytes and fluids; it also has an important role in the regulation of blood pressure and blood cell production.

- The ED 12 Infoceutical assists with the maturation process of lymphocytes and monocytes (white blood cells).

ED 13 – Immunity Driver

The immune system protects the body from constant intrusion by toxic factors of both external and internal sources. The Immunity Driver field is mostly formed by the action of the bone marrow as it generates immune cells; however, the spleen drives the creation of immune cells within the bone marrow, so its field is also part of the Immune Driver.

- The ED 13 Infoceutical has been designed to restore integrity to the Immunity Driver field and thus assists in the generation of immune cells. These can take from a few days to a month to mature into functional units.

- The effects of the ED13 Infoceutical take time to become apparent and so it should be taken in low doses for at least one month.

- The Immune Driver field is linked with many immune cells including the stimulation of blastic cells, maturation of reticulocytes, long-term immunity mylocytes (bone marrow cells that produce granular corpuscles), macrophages (that ingest foreign particles), mast cells, lymph cells (of which there are many types), red blood cells, as well as the many types of white blood cells. (T cells, however, are associated with the Thymus Driver.)

- The ED 13 Infoceutical is used with care in specific situations (outlined in NES practitioner training).

ED 14 – Thymus Driver

The thymus plays a major role in the immune system throughout life and aids the creation of immune cells and the production of long-term antibodies. While the bone marrow develops the majority of white blood cells (Immunity Driver), the thymus is concerned with T-lymphocytes cells, which aid the recognition and rejection of foreign tissue (antigens).

- The ED 14 Infoceutical has been designed to support the Thymus Driver field and its function of antibody formation.

- The thymus is directly associated with T-helper cells (amplify antibody production), T-suppressor cells (reduce overactive immune function) and natural killer cells (destroy invading antigens).

- The Thymus Driver field is associated with the maturation of myelocytes (cells in the bone marrow).

ED 15 – Pancreas Driver

The pancreas produces a complex cocktail of carbohydrate, protein and fat digestive enzymes. Hormones secreted by glands on the surface of the pancreas play a vital role in blood sugar regulation. The Pancreas Driver field is generated by both the digestive and endocrine functions of the pancreas. The pancreas is very sensitive to environmental toxins, which can disturb its functions.

- The ED 15 Infoceutical has been designed to restore integrity to the Pancreas Driver field.

- ED 15 may help people with no appetite, poor digestion, headaches and pains in the pancreas.

- Those with an allopathic diagnosis of hypoglycaemia will often find that Pancreas Driver shows up in the NES scan. Restoring the field may help them go longer between meals without feeling queasy.

- The Pancreas Driver field assists with the maturation process of lymphocytes in the spleen.

- The pancreas is a favored site for most Energetic Terrains, and it often shows up on the NES scan for this reason. Thus, using the ED 15 Infoceutical may stimulate the energetic elimination of latent or chronic viral conditions. For this reason, it is usually not used in the first visit, or until the individual's vitality is more robust.

ED 16 – Bone Driver

This field is a combination of three other Drivers: Liver, Kidney and Pancreas, which together form a new energetic unit, called Bone Driver. Heavy metals, particularly lead, mercury and aluminium, tend to collect in the bones and so this field is strongly linked to heavy metals. Bone Driver field affects calcium metabolism in muscles (including cardiac) as well as bones.

- The ED 16 Infoceutical has been designed to aid the removal of heavy metals from bone tissue.

- The ED 16 Infoceutical may assist in normalizing calcium metabolism (many metallic toxins in the body bond with calcium).

- Calcium exists in all cells and is involved in muscular contraction, intercellular communication (virtual), transmission of nerve impulses, hormone release and blood coagulation. Calcium also builds up in the arteries and as stones.

- The ED 16 Infoceutical may benefit toxic issues that have contributed to swelling of the heart.

- The ED 16 Infoceutical can aid the drainage of toxins that have migrated to the extremities (hands and feet) instead of being released from the body.

- The ED 16 Infoceutical may aid the normalizing of the appetite.

- The Bone Driver field assists with the maturation of erythrocytes (red blood cells) and is involved with the antibody system generally.

Energetic Star 15 (Heavy Metals) (the Energetic Stars are not addressed in this book) can be used to extend the activity of Bone Driver to rid unwanted metals from the bones.

The Energetic Integrators

According to NES bioenergetic theory, the human body-field is responsible for overall coordination and regulation of all physical, chemical, neural and energetic activity within the body. To perform this coordination and regulation role, the body-field divides into 12 energy "compartments" known in NES as Energetic Integrators (EIs).

- Each Integrator is responsible for regulating discrete activates in the body. In the software, to view the regulatory functions of an EI you click on its bar graph.

- Information transfer is vital for the correct functioning of the body. Every cell, tissue and organ needs to be directed and coordinated in its activity.

- The Integrators have a directing role in ensuring that the correct regulatory information reaches its required destination. The Integrators can be considered to form "route maps" for QED information transfer all over the body.

- The cells, tissues and organs interpret the information passed on to them so that they may act in a coordinated manner according to the body's needs.

- The 12 Integrators to some extent correspond with the 12 acupuncture meridians of Tradition Chinese Medicine, but this only a small aspect of their makeup.

- Energetic Integrators can become damaged or distorted by a number of factors including toxins, microbes, radiation, shocks and stress.

- If an Integrator is distorted, its information transfer mechanism becomes compromised and some of the information it is responsible for may not all reach the required site. This will result in incorrect or sub-optimal coordination of body processes.

- The NES–Professional™ detects and reports on the state of the 12 Integrators within the main screen of the assessment software. The more distorted an Integrator is the higher the reading.

- The NES EI Infoceuticals (oral preparations) are designed to correct distortions in Integrator fields, restoring integrity to their function and thus harmonizing the body processes they regulate.

Using the Energetic Integrator Infoceuticals

The full use of EI Infoceuticals, including dosages, is covered in the NES online advanced certificate training program.

- Due to the fundamental need to ensure correct coordination and regulation of body processes, the Energetic Integrators are given priority attention in the NES treatment protocol.

- The EI Infoceuticals are normally first used in the second NES treatment along with ED (Energetic Driver) Infoceuticals. They are also frequently used in subsequent treatments.

- The EI Infoceuticals are used in order in any protocol, corresponding to their number. The lower number is taken before the next higher number.

- Normally 2 or a maximum of 3 EI Infoceuticals would be used in any one protocol, with each taken at least 10 minutes apart.

Energetic Integrator 1 Neurosensory –
Large Intestine Meridian

Energetic Integrator 1 is associated with the regulation of many body functions including those listed below. The EI 1 Infoceutical has been designed to restore integrity to this integrator where field errors have disrupted its function.

Keynotes

- Nervous system Cranial nerves and sensory receptors
- Large intestine function and mineral absorption
- Ears, nose, throat

Energetic Integrator 2 Heart - Lung Meridians

Energetic Integrator 2 is associated with the regulation of many body functions including those listed below. The EI 2 Infoceutical has been designed to restore integrity to this integrator where field errors have disrupted its function.

Keynotes

- Cardiac tissue and heart function
- Lung physiology and heart-lung interaction

Energetic Integrator 3 Mucous Membranes – Small Intestine Meridian

Energetic Integrator 3 is associated with the regulation of many body functions including those listed below. The EI 3 Infoceutical has been designed to restore integrity to this integrator where field errors have disrupted its function

Keynotes

- Small intestines, organs and meridian
- Calcium metabolism and bones
- Vertebra
- Mucous membranes of the gut, nose, throat, lungs, etc.; skin.

Energetic Integrator 4 Neurotransmitters – Heart Meridian

Energetic Integrator 4 is associated with the regulation of many body functions including those listed below. The EI 4 Infoceutical has been designed to restore integrity to this integrator where field errors have disrupted its function.

Keynotes

- Neurotransmitters and midbrain

- Uterus and ovaries
- Audio acuity learning

Energetic Integrator 5 Lymphatics – Bladder Meridian

Energetic Integrator 5 is associated with the regulation of many body functions including those listed below. The EI 5 Infoceutical has been designed to restore integrity to this integrator where field errors have disrupted its function.

Keynotes

- Lymph: drainage, nodes and lymphocytes
- Hormones: adrenals, pituitary, thyroid
- Vertebra
- Bladder
- Male genitalia

Energetic Integrator 6 Kidney – Kidney Meridian

Energetic Integrator 6 is associated with the regulation of many body functions including those listed below. The EI 6 Infoceutical has been designed to restore integrity to this integrator where field errors have disrupted its function.

Keynotes

- Kidney organ and kidney meridian
- Acid-Alkaline or pH regulation
- Pineal gland and precursor hormones (DHEA)
- Neurological tissue (white matter)

Energetic Integrator 7 Blood Field – Gall Bladder Meridian

Energetic Integrator 7 is associated with the regulation of many body functions including those listed below. The EI 7 Infoceutical has been designed to restore integrity to this integrator where field errors have disrupted its function.

Keynotes

- Blood cell production
- Blood pressure regulation
- Immune activation, T and NK cells
- Upper GI digestion, gall bladder function
- Motor neurons and gray matter function

Energetic Integrator 8 Microbes – Liver Meridian

Energetic Integrator 8 is associated with the regulation of many body functions including those listed below. The EI 8 Infoceutical has been designed to restore integrity to this integrator where field errors have disrupted its function.

Keynotes

- Energetic Terrains: microbial disease
- Vision; eye conditions
- Hormonal components, including estrogens

Energetic Integrator 9 Thyroid – Triple Burner Meridian

Energetic Integrator 9 is associated with the regulation of many body functions including those listed below. The EI 9 Infoceutical has been designed to restore integrity to this integrator where field errors have disrupted its function.

Keynotes

- Thyroid gland and thyroid function

- Links the three primary body cavities: cranium, thorax and abdominal

Energetic Integrator 10 Circulation – Heart Protector Meridian

Energetic Integrator 10 is associated with the regulation of many body functions including those listed below. The EI 10 Infoceutical has been designed to restore integrity to this integrator where field errors have disrupted its function.

Keynotes

- Circulatory system: arterial and venous

- Neuroendocrine regulation

- Motor, visual and auditory regulation (midbrain)

- Anti-inflammatory effects

Energetic Integrator 11 Bone Marrow – Stomach Meridian

Energetic Integrator 11 is associated with the regulation of many body functions including those listed below. The EI 11 Infoceutical has been designed to restore integrity to this integrator where field errors have disrupted its function.

Keynotes

- Stomach & digestion

- Harbors heavy metals

- Bone marrow

- Male sexual system

Energetic Integrator 12 Shock – Spleen Meridian

Energetic Integrator 12 is associated with the regulation of many body functions including those listed below. The EI 12 Infoceutical has been designed to restore integrity to this integrator where field errors have disrupted its function.

Keynotes

- Collapse, shock, exhaustion

- Digestive function, digestive enzymes

- Pancreas: sugar metabolism

- Toxic effects of radiation and radioactive substances (ionizing radiation, X-rays, microwaves) and of shock (physical, emotional, chemical), geopathic stress, solvents, and fungicides/pesticides.

Concluding Remarks from Harry Massey

Our intention with the NES–Professional™ health is to begin to unite the traditional theories of allopathic medicine, physics, and biology with alternative theories about the QED aspects of the human body. We see this book as a first attempt to stimulate discussion and further research between the various disciplines so that an overall model of human functioning can be refined and improved upon. We do not claim by any means to have all the answers. Peter and I did not have a large research department working for us whilst formulating this theory; in fact, it was all done on a much-stretched shoestring budget. However, every single statement about the NES theory of the human body-field in this book is based on Peter's repeated testing over a 25-year period and together we continue to do research into the nature, cause and treatment of disease from the energetic (QED) level.

NES–Professional™ came about because of the personal fight of two men against illness; however, there is another side to our interest. I have been saddened for years by what I can see around me: mainly poor health, war, poverty, and the destruction of the environment. To me, at my darkest moments, our health and our world seem unsustainable over the long term. In my brightest moments, I, like so many of you reading this book, seek ways to reverse these trends, although we often feel powerless to do so.

From where do these problems stem? Very simply, there is a general lack of human awareness of the interconnectedness of all things. As mentioned in the early chapters of this book, reality is not as simple as the four-dimensional world that we live and breathe in daily. Rather, it is a complex interaction between consciousness and all matter, and everything is interconnected.

An overall shift in human awareness (and responsibility) can only occur if each of us, as an individual, becomes more conscious, and consequently healthier. It should be fairly obvious to you, after reading this book, that major health gains that can be made via the NES–Professional™, but it is perhaps not so obvious (as it has not been included in this text) of the effects this can have on consciousness. Higher consciousness in terms of quantum biology is an optimum body-field, where all mental, visual, auditory, emotional and psychic abilities are working at their full and natural capacity. The heightening of the health of your body-field leads to a greater awareness of your interconnectedness with the Universe, which, of course, has massive behavioural implications for the good of all.

It is my hope that through the spread of the NES–Professional™ more and more people will begin to understand that what benefits each of us, also benefits the whole. As our behaviour begins to shift towards health for ourselves, kindness towards each other, and respect for the environment, then the world will become a better place for us all.

Thank you for reading.

Harry Massey

Client and Practitioner Testimonials

Clients

Because my job was fairly sedentary, working in an office from 9 to 5, I decided to increase my aerobic fitness by taking up cycling after work. After several months my energy disappeared, and I could barely ride my push bike around the block. I decided to contact Peter Fraser. The NES results were not very encouraging. Indications were that my body had been poisoned by some type of dioxin, a poison, which I knew to be produced and released in a nearby chemical processing factory. It was fortunate that Peter Fraser and the Infoceuticals got my liver (Cell Driver) working again. My health and general levels of vitality improved dramatically in the years following my various treatments from Peter Fraser. My grey hair stopped falling out. I have transformed myself from a listless 52-year-old office worker who barely had enough energy to get out of bed each morning to a 54-year-old office worker who has just finished participating in his second gruelling nine-day bicycle marathon, covering up to 600 kilometres during each event. My wife and my friends look at me and ask me where I get my energy from. I just tell them about Peter Fraser and his research into quantum biology.

North Queensland, Australia

I first met Peter in Merimbula a number of years ago and was privileged to watch him work one morning in his home laboratory. I was particularly impressed with the amount of painstaking work he undertook and how careful he was with his analysis. I then asked him to run a test of me ... and I obviously didn't tell him any of my history. I was astonished to discover how much he knew about my health, which could not have been apparent to the eye. For example, he pointed out some long-standing conditions like increasing osteoporosis and weak digestive system. He was also able to warn me that I might be developing diverticulitis, and although I hadn't had an attack at that time, I unfortunately fulfilled his predictions a year later. I have consulted with Peter intermittently and each time he has been able to give me a remarkable snapshot of my health—or lack of it—and seems to be able to be quite specific. Several times I have experienced a remarkable upturn in my general health after using his magical, odourless, colourless drops [Infoceuticals]. I wish him well in his continued important research work, and believe he is an inspirational leader in his field.

J. B.

I started taking the drops this morning and IMMEDIATELY felt stuff happening in my head! Quite extraordinary. The depression, or feeling of malaise that there is something awfully wrong with me, lifted in minutes and I feel renewed strength that I can get better. Thanks for the encouragement.

Ms. O.B.

I am a long-term practising Health Professional. For the last 21 years I have been acquainted with Peter Fraser. I have many times been inspired by his progress into the field of quantum medicine. Throughout his many years of tortuous heavy thinking, meditation and deep insight, Peter maintained a practical path of conventional study and research. I have been a firsthand recipient and many-time witness, through my clientele, to the implementation of his findings – via his "drops" – and have repeatedly found the results truly awesome.

I would like to give a couple of my own personal experiences as examples. One of the most remarkable treatments I have received was in the Victorian winter of 1991 when I suffered a very severe chest infection. The doctors were useless. I truly thought I would die and felt that my body had no resistance.

Peter tested me and suggested "haemophalis" virus, which is carried by parrots. From the instant ... the Infoceuticals hit my tongue I felt my body's defence mechanisms kick in and within a very short time I fully recovered.

On another occasion I found a lump in my right breast and consulted conventional doctors, who recommended a mammogram, to which I had a strong aversion as I instinctively felt that any radiation at that time would have a detrimental effect on already distressed tissues. I went along for an ultrasound and explained to the radiographer why I did not want a mammogram. He said that it was all in my head! I stuck to my instincts and consulted Peter, who found [the energetic signature of] a pre-cancerous condition and provided me with a series of drops plus advice on lifestyle, diet, supplements, etc. I only took the drops, nothing else in my life changed. I had all sorts of weird emotions and dreams, issues, I guess being resolved: my mother having died of breast cancer. Within a period of about 10 weeks my lump and my fear disappeared.

A. Jane Webber

I have been using the Nutri-Energetic [Infoceuticals] over the last few weeks and have been very impressed. I experienced an immediate change the first time I tried them and have noticed ongoing improvements ever since. I especially have more energy and am experiencing continued improvement with chronic systemic conditions.

Dr. C. P.

About 5 years ago I started to develop an allergy or two, causing headaches, runny nose, etc. Also a rash all over my body. About 3 years ago, I started to develop classic symptoms of fibromyalgia: pain in the hands to shoulders, feet to hips, plus tightness in the head. I have always been a good sleeper (night or day) until 7 months ago, when my brain just decided to power on at night (every night) not allowing a good night's sleep. There has also been a feeling of total fatigue. Examples, at the end of a day's work, within 10 minutes, my body powers down to exhaustion. According to a series of blood tests, etc., I am impressively healthy, except for the fibromyalgia. I have resisted taking painkillers, sleeping pills, etc. Since taking the Nutri-Energetics Infoceuticals, the pain has eased in my limbs, my head does not feel as tight, my brain does not power on at night. I also feel mentally brighter and am continuing to make progress.

Corenne Shanks, Australia, aged 59

I have to say that Peter Fraser's scan and Infoceuticals have helped me immensely over the last few years. When I was recently in hospital with pneumonia and was really on my last legs, Peter was right on target with the Nutri-Energetics Infoceuticals – my lungs cleared up and I did not need to go back to hospital as the doctor said I probably would.

I have had an existing eye problem for a very long time – 10 to 12 years at least, which was a mystery to the doctors and ophthalmologists. Peter got to the root of the problem, finding the [energetic imprint of] a virus affecting the brain, which the doctors could not accept. I found the Infoceuticals of great benefit. My hearing also improved quite dramatically.

Dr. S. L.

I am a total newbie to all of this. I am writing because my daughter's acupuncturist had me try some type of test on his computer [NES]; he then told me I was out of balance. All this is over my head, but what is happening to me [from using the Infoceuticals] is absolutely amazing. I'm experiencing improved memory and bursts of unbelievable creativity (I am an artist). I am not procrastinating when it comes to the

household bills and instead I have become this organizing
fanatic. I have never been organized, despite a bookshelf full of
books on getting organized. I don't need coffee all day, like I
used to, am sleeping better and my moods are more even

A.M., Los Angeles, CA

NES Practitioners

I have been using NES for almost a year. I have had diabetes
Type I for 46 years, fibromyalgia, osteoarthritis, and many other
ailments. I had been diagnosed with the end of stage three,
beginning of stage four, kidney disease. I have been on the
Infoceutical protocols for eight months. My kidney disease has
miraculously reversed to stage one. The medical doctors cannot
find any reason that I would have kidney disease, and cannot
explain the reversal. I no longer suffer from fibromyalgia nor do
I have any pain from arthritis. I am a brittle diabetic, and my
need for insulin has decreased greatly, and my body's ability to
handle high glucose foods has improved.

As for my clients, I just started a 52-year-old woman on the NES
program. For years she has suffered from uncontrollable
hypertension. In spite of the many high-blood pressure
medications the doctors have prescribed, her readings remained
very high. Within two weeks of using the Infoceuticals, she let
us know that for the first time in six years her blood pressure
now registers in the normal range.

Another case: I have been seeing a 45-year-old woman for two
months. She suffers from major depression and has been
diagnosed with bi-polar disease. She was plagued with fatigue,
aches and pains, thoughts of suicide, and extreme anxiety.
After using NES, this woman now has much more energy and
hope for the future. All symptoms are gradually disappearing,

and she has the will to live. In her words, "Something is working for the first time in my life!"

Lorilyn K. Lachman, NES Practitioner

Wanted to pass on some positive anecdotal clinical feedback. I had a gentleman present one month ago with chronic hypertension, averaging 170's/90 for quite some time. He was on medication but went off due to side effects. NES showed Cell Driver and Liver Driver, and that's all I put him on. He followed up with me yesterday and for the last 2 weeks he has been averaging 130's and even 120's/80's. Follow-up test showed Cell Driver and Liver Driver at 0. This does emphasize the importance that if folks are on blood pressure medication, they need to be aware that their pressure may drop and they may need to wean off of their medication. This gentleman decided to go off himself long before he saw me, and hence he had a very high level coming in, which gave me a perfect opportunity to assess effectiveness.

Another gentleman presented with a dx of acute bladder infection and refused to take an antibiotic. I did not tell him not to take antibiotic as that is his choice. Top items of the whole test: EI 5 (bladder/lymph), EI 8 (microbes), Liver Driver.

A woman presented with Chronic Fatigue Syndrome. Among other things, iron was deviated on Nutritional screen by 2. She saw her GP right after seeing me, and subsequent blood work showed low iron and ferritin. She mentioned that I had suggested she might be low in iron; her doctor wondered how a computer could know that...

Jason Siczkowycz, ND, NES Practitioner

My client is a mother, wife and author. She nearly died from taking contaminated L-Tryptophan (it was a genetically altered bacteria that has to date never been identified) distributed by a single manufacturer in the 1980's. Eosinophilia-Myalgia Syndrome (EMS) is a complex systemic syndrome that is directly associated with this L-Tryptophan contamination. Nearly 50 people died in the first year alone. My client was almost one of them. She has had related health problems for 16 years, including Fibromyalgia Syndrome, Chronic Fatigue Syndrome, neuropathy (now peripheral), and a lung issue. She reports battling depression intermittently over the past decade or more, and has body aches and pains, recurring low-grade fevers, autoimmune problems, and in recent years an under-active thyroid, mild colitis, and was recently diagnosed with a fatty liver. She reports that she cannot concentrate and easily becomes fatigued.

After only two protocols with the NES, she is experiencing great relief from her symptoms. She recently wrote: "I just can't believe how much more energy I have. Today I had devotions and breakfast, went to Curves for a workout, came home and showered and did my hair, went to the school to mentor my "at risk" 10-year-old mentee for an hour, met a friend for lunch, went shopping with her on the spur of the moment, came home, rested for thirty minutes, met someone for a quick dinner, went to a one-hour rumba dance class, came home, rested, showered, and am now e-mailing you. You have no idea how impossible that would have been anytime in the last 16 years! I'm just afraid to believe it is true! ... I'm thrilled to be so active. There is no way I can thank you for all you are doing for me."

Randi Eaton, LMBT, NES Practitioner